Raintree Steck-Vaughn

Illustrated
SCIENCE
ENCYCLOPEDIA

Volume
22

VIP – ZYG

RSVP
**RAINTREE
STECK-VAUGHN**
P U B L I S H E R S
The Steck-Vaughn Company

Austin, Texas

Published by Raintree Steck-Vaughn Publishers, an imprint of Steck-Vaughn Company.

Executive Editor	Diane Sharpe
Senior Editor	Anne Souby
Design Manager	Joyce Spicer

This edition edited and designed by Andromeda Oxford Ltd.

Andromeda Editorial and Design

Project Manager	Julia Roles
Editorial Manager	Jenny Fry
Design	TT Designs, T&S Truscott
Cover Design	John Barker

Library of Congress Cataloging-in-Publication Data
Raintree Steck-Vaughn illustrated science encyclopedia.
        p.   cm.
    Includes bibliographical references and index.
    Summary: A twenty-four volume set containing brief articles on science topics.
    ISBN 0-8172-3943-X (set)
    ISBN 0-8172-3940-5 (Volume 22)
    1. Science—Encyclopedias, Juvenile.   [1. Science—Encyclopedias.]   I. Raintree Steck-Vaughn Publishers.
Q121.R354   1997
503—dc20   96-11078
                                        CIP
                                        AC

Printed and Bound in the United States of America.
1 2 3 4 5 6 7 8 9 10 IP 00 99 98 97 96

USING THE RAINTREE STECK-VAUGHN ILLUSTRATED SCIENCE ENCYCLOPEDIA

You are living in a world in which science, technology, and nature are very important. You see something about science almost every day. It might be on television, in the newspaper, in a book at school, or some other place. Often, you want more information about what you see.

The *Raintree Steck-Vaughn Illustrated Science Encyclopedia* will help you find what you want to know. It contains information on many science subjects. You may want to find out about computers, the environment, space exploration, biology, agriculture, or mathematics, for example. They are all in the *Raintree Steck-Vaughn Illustrated Science Encyclopedia*. There are many, many other subjects covered as well.

There are twenty-four volumes in the encyclopedia. The articles, which are called entries, are in alphabetical order through the first twenty-two volumes. On the spine of each volume, below the volume number, are some letters. The letters above the line are the first three letters of the first entry in that volume. The letters below the line are the first three letters of the last entry in that volume. In Volume 1, for example, you see that the first entry begins with **AAR** and that the last entry begins with **ANT**. Using the letters makes it easy to find the volume you need.

In Volume 23, there are three special features—reference charts and tables, a bibliography, and an index. In Volume 24, there are interesting projects that you can do on your own. The projects are fun to do, and they help you discover and understand important science principles. Many can give you ideas that can help you develop your own science fair projects.

Main Entries There are two kinds of main entries in the *Raintree Steck-Vaughn Illustrated Science Encyclopedia*. Many of the entries are major topics that are spread over several pages. The titles of these entries are shown at the top of the page in a yellow box. Other entries required less space to cover the topic fully. The titles of these main entries are printed in capital letters. They look like this: **ABALONE**. At the beginning of some entries, you will see a phonetic pronunciation of the entry title, such as (ăb′ ə lō′ nē).

In the front of each volume, there is a pronunciation key. Use it the same way you use your dictionary's pronunciation key.

Cross-References Within the main entries are cross-references referring to other entries in the encyclopedia. Within an entry, they look like this: (see MAMMAL). At the end of an entry, they look like this: *See also* HYENA. These cross-references tell you where to find other helpful information on the subject you are reading about.

Projects At the end of some entries, you will see this symbol: PROJECT 1. It tells you which projects related to that entry are in Volume 24.

Illustrations There are thousands of photographs, drawings, graphs, diagrams, tables, and other illustrations in the *Raintree Steck-Vaughn Illustrated Science Encyclopedia*. They will help you better understand the entries you read. Captions describe the illustrations. Many of the illustrations also have labels that point out important parts.

Activities Some main entries include activities presented in a special box. These activities are short projects that give you a chance to work with science on your own.

Index In Volume 23, the index lists every main entry by volume and page number. Many subjects that are not main entries are also listed in the index, as well as the illustrations, projects, activities, and reference charts and tables.

Bibliography In Volume 23, there is also a bibliography for students. The books in this list are on a variety of topics and can supplement what you have learned in the *Raintree Steck-Vaughn Illustrated Science Encyclopedia*.

The *Raintree Steck-Vaughn Illustrated Science Encyclopedia* was designed especially for you, the student. It is a source of knowledge for the world of science, technology, and nature. Enjoy it!

PRONUNCIATION KEY

Each symbol has the same sound as the darker letters in the sample words.

ə	balloon, ago	îr	deer, pier	r	root, tire
ă	map, have	j	join, germ	s	so, press
ā	day, made	k	king, ask	sh	shoot, machine
âr	care, bear	l	let, cool	t	to, stand
ä	father, car	m	man, same	th	thin, death
b	ball, rib	n	no, turn	*th*	then, this
ch	choose, nature	ng	bring, long	ŭ	up, cut
d	did, add	ŏ	odd, pot	ûr	urge, hurt
ĕ	bell, get	ō	cone, know	v	view, give
ē	sweet, easy	ô	all, saw	w	wood, glowing
f	fan, soft	oi	boy, boil	y	yes, year
g	good, big	ou	now, loud	z	zero, raise
h	hurt, ahead	o͝o	good, took	zh	leisure, vision
ĭ	rip, ill	o͞o	boot, noon	'	strong accent
ī	side, sky	p	part, scrap	ˊ	weak accent

GUIDE TO MEASUREMENT ABBREVIATIONS

All measurements in the *Raintree Steck-Vaughn Illustrated Science Encyclopedia* are given in both the customary system and the metric system [in brackets like these]. Following are the abbreviations used for various units of measure.

Customary Units of Measure

mi. = miles	cu. yd. = cubic yards
m.p.h. = miles per hour	cu. ft. = cubic feet
yd. = yards	cu. in. = cubic inches
ft. = feet	gal. = gallons
in. = inches	pt. = pints
sq. mi. = square miles	qt. = quarts
sq. yd. = square yards	lb. = pounds
sq. ft. = square feet	oz. = ounces
sq. in. = square inches	fl. oz. = fluid ounces
cu. mi. = cubic miles	°F = degrees Fahrenheit

Metric Units of Measure

km = kilometers	cu. km = cubic kilometers
kph = kilometers per hour	cu. m = cubic meters
m = meters	cu. cm = cubic centimeters
cm = centimeters	ml = milliliters
mm = millimeters	kg = kilograms
sq. km = square kilometers	g = grams
sq. m = square meters	mg = milligrams
sq. cm = square centimeters	°C = degrees Celsius

For information on how to convert customary measurements to metric measurements, see the Metric Conversions table in Volume 23.

VIPER A viper is any of a number of poisonous snakes belonging to the family Viperidae. True vipers are found in Africa, Asia, and Europe.

Vipers have two hollow fangs (long teeth) in the upper jaw. These fangs carry poison into the body of an animal bitten by the snake. The fangs are folded back along the roof of the mouth when the mouth is shut, but they swing forward when the mouth opens. The poison is formed in special glands (see GLAND).

Most vipers have thick bodies and short tails and markedly triangular heads. Most true vipers do not lay eggs but instead bring forth live young.

Pit vipers differ from true vipers in having heat-sensitive pits on the snout. Pit vipers live in the Americas and in Asia, and they include the rattlesnake.

See also SNAKE.

VIPER
Vipers use their fangs to inject poison to stun and kill the rodents and other small animals on which they feed. Pictured is a desert horned viper, a type of true viper.

VIREO (vîr′ē ō′) A vireo is a small bird of the family Vireonidae. There are forty-six species, twelve of them living in North America. They are mostly dull colored, with a gray, brown, or olive back and wings and a white or yellow belly. The bill is relatively thick and has a tiny hook at the end.

Most vireos are 4 to 6 in. [10 to 15 cm] long. They feed on insects.

VIREO
Twelve of the forty-six species of vireos live in North America. Pictured here is a red-eyed vireo at its nest.

VIRGINIA CREEPER Virginia creeper is a vigorous climbing plant in the vine family. Sometimes called American ivy or woodbine, it grows throughout the United States. Although similar to poison ivy, the leaves of the plant have five, not three, leaflets that turn red in the fall (see POISONOUS PLANT). It is a popular plant for growing on house and garden walls.

The Virginia creeper climbs by means of tendrils. Each tendril branches into several smaller tendrils. Each of the smaller tendrils ends in a disklike sucker pad that attaches to an object as the plant grows.

See also TENDRIL; VINE FAMILY.

VIRUS A virus is a microorganism that lives in a cell of another living thing. Viruses can be seen only with an electron microscope (see CELL; ELECTRON MICROSCOPE; MICROORGANISM). They range in size from about 0.01 to 0.3 micron. (One micron equals 0.000039 in. or 0.001 mm.) Viruses are a major cause of disease. Recently discovered particles called viroids and prions, which are even smaller than viruses, have also been found to cause disease (see DISEASE).

A virus particle consists of protein and either DNA or RNA. Viruses containing RNA are called retroviruses. By itself, a virus is lifeless and cannot reproduce. However, once it is inside a living cell, a virus becomes an active organism that can multiply hundreds of times. It uses the materials in the cells for itself, and this is why the virus causes disease or illness. Thus, unlike bacteria, viruses cannot be grown in a nonliving substance, but must be bred in the laboratory on living tissue (see BACTERIA; DNA; PROTEIN; RNA).

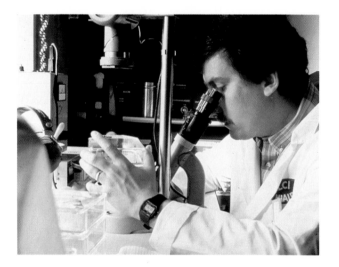

VIRUS

Viruses, such as the vaccinia virus (right), cause various diseases—vaccinia causes cowpox. A virologist (above) is a scientist who studies viruses.

Virus diseases Both plants and animals are attacked by viruses. In most cases, the diseases can occur only in certain organisms or groups of organisms. For example, fowl pest, swine fever, and distemper are virus diseases of animals that human beings cannot catch. However, cowpox, rabies, and psittacosis (a disease of birds) can be passed on to human beings. Among the many other human virus diseases are AIDS, the common cold, influenza, polio, chicken pox, smallpox, mumps, measles, shingles, and hepatitis. Some kinds of cancer such as leukemia also may be caused by viruses. Virus diseases of plants, such as various mosaic diseases, destroy many crops. Viruses known as bacteriophages even attack bacteria (see BACTERIO-PHAGE).

There is very little that physicians can do to treat virus diseases directly. They can treat the effects of the disease and any complications that may arise. However, few drugs have been discovered that really work against viruses in the way that antibiotics fight bacteria (see ANTIBIOTIC). A person's body does, however, fight against invading viruses. It produces antibodies that work to destroy the viruses. Also, the body produces a substance called interferon whenever viruses are present in the body. Interferon helps keep viruses from spreading from cell to cell (see ANTIBODY; IMMUNITY; INTERFERON). Recently, scientists have been able to make interferon artificially through cloning and other

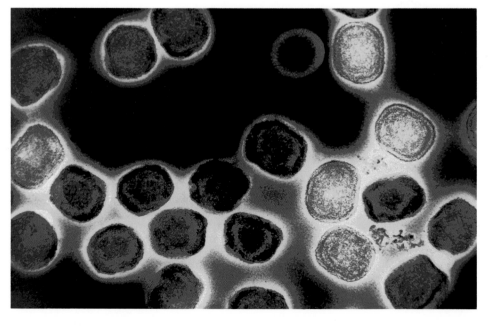

techniques (see CLONE). For example, they have been able to make human cells produce interferon by adding certain foreign substances to them. Now, with larger quantities of interferon to work with, researchers have a better chance of finding ways to treat virus diseases directly.

Currently, the only way to prevent virus disease is by use of vaccines (see VACCINATION). Vaccinations involve placing dead or weakened viruses in a person's body. This stimulates the body to produce antibodies. Thus, the body develops immunity to the virus disease. Also, once a person has had a virus disease, his or her body always retains some ability to form the correct antibodies quickly if a second attack occurs. Thus, such diseases may affect a person only once.

Virologists are scientists who study viruses. They study viruses chiefly to learn how the organisms cause disease and how to control these organisms. Scientists also use viruses for such purposes as insect control, cell research, and development of vaccines.

See also MICROBIOLOGY.

VIRUS, COMPUTER A computer virus is a piece of a computer program, or code, that inserts itself into an existing computer program (see COMPUTER). Usually, the user does not realize a virus is present. Once inside the program, the virus causes problems by changing or destroying data, or changing the way the original program works. Like living viruses, computer viruses can "replicate," or reproduce themselves, and "infect," or spread to, other computers through shared disks. Viruses can also spread through and disable a computer network.

The United States government and many states have passed laws making it illegal to introduce computer viruses that spread into the computers of unsuspecting users. To offer further protection, computer software companies also design special antivirus programs that check disks and incoming files to make sure they do not contain viruses. These programs have to be updated very frequently in order to be effective, because new computer viruses are constantly being created.

See also SOFTWARE.

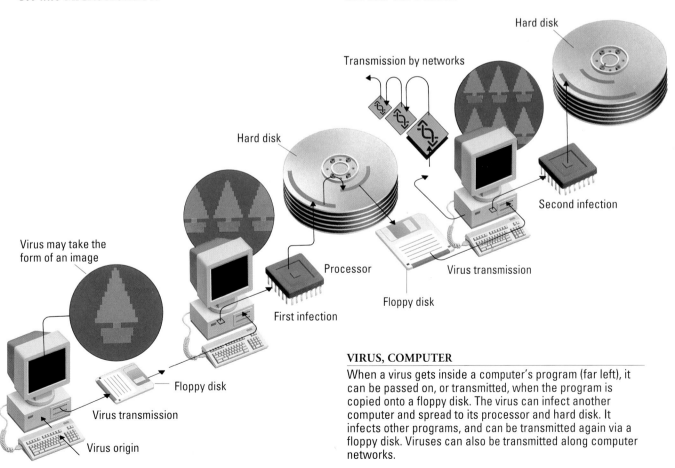

VIRUS, COMPUTER

When a virus gets inside a computer's program (far left), it can be passed on, or transmitted, when the program is copied onto a floppy disk. The virus can infect another computer and spread to its processor and hard disk. It infects other programs, and can be transmitted again via a floppy disk. Viruses can also be transmitted along computer networks.

VISCOSITY (vĭ skŏs'ĭ tē) Viscosity is the resistance of a liquid or a gas to an object moving through it. The greater the viscosity of a substance, the more it resists an object moving through it. For example, if a stone is dropped into water, it sinks fairly quickly. The same stone would sink much more slowly in oil. Oil is more viscous than water. When an object falls through a liquid or a gas, it eventually reaches a maximum speed. This speed is called its terminal velocity (see TERMINAL VELOCITY). The more viscous the liquid or gas, the lower the terminal velocity of an object moving through it. Viscosity also affects the rate at which a liquid can be poured. Water can be poured more quickly than can oil. This is because water is less viscous.

To understand viscosity, think of a liquid or gas as being made up of thin layers. Viscosity is caused by friction between these layers (see FRICTION). An object falling through a liquid or gas is slowed down by friction between it and the liquid or gas.

The viscosity of a liquid decreases as its temperature increases. The viscosity of a gas, however, increases as its temperature increases.

VITAMIN Vitamins are organic (carbon-containing) compounds needed in small amounts to support life. Vitamins do not supply energy. However, they do help the body release energy from carbohydrates, fats, and proteins (see CARBOHYDRATE; COMPOUND; FAT; PROTEIN). They also play an important role in many chemical reactions throughout the body. The steady absence of one vitamin in an otherwise complete diet causes a deficiency disease, such as scurvy (see DEFICIENCY DISEASES; DIET; NUTRITION; SCURVY).

It is best to obtain vitamins by eating the foods in which they naturally occur. There are also pills, capsules, and liquids available that contain a single vitamin or a combination of vitamins. A person should consult his or her physician before taking any of these. Too much of a vitamin can, in some cases, be as dangerous as too little.

There are two basic groups of vitamins. The vitamins in one group dissolve in fat. They are called the fat-soluble group. Vitamins A, D, E, and K belong to this group. The vitamins in the other group, called the water-soluble vitamins, dissolve in water. Vitamin C and the eight B-complex vitamins belong to this group. The B-complex vitamins are biotin, folic acid (folacin), niacin, pantothenic acid, riboflavin, thiamine, vitamin B_6, and vitamin B_{12}.

Vitamin A is needed for growth, healthy skin, and good night vision. Vitamin D is important for strong bones and teeth. Vitamin D is formed in

VITAMIN

Citrus fruits are rich in vitamin C, particularly varieties of oranges (top) and grapefruits (bottom). Also called ascorbic acid, vitamin C is one of the water-soluble vitamins.

skin that is exposed to sunlight. Vitamin E helps maintain cell membranes (see CELL). Vitamin K is necessary for blood clotting (see BLOOD). Vitamin C, or ascorbic acid, prevents and cures scurvy. The B vitamins play many important roles. They help release energy from digested food. They are important in maintaining a healthy nervous system and normal blood. Thiamine is needed to prevent beriberi, a disease of the nervous system. A deficiency of niacin causes the disease pellagra. Pellagra causes a person to have indigestion, fatigue, pale skin, and a swollen tongue. Deficiencies of folic acid and vitamin B_{12} can cause anemia (see ANEMIA).

VOICE The voice is the sound reproduced by the larynx and changed by the vocal mechanism (see LARYNX; SOUND). In humans, the vocal mechanism consists of the vocal cords (two folds of tissue in the larynx, which stretch to alter the sound), the tongue, and the mouth. Nearly all land-based animals that have a larynx use the voice to communicate. Mammals and birds have highly developed patterns of sound (language) that can communicate complex messages, such as warnings of danger or mating calls (see BIRD; MAMMAL). In humans, the voice is developed to the point of communicating thoughts and feelings. Children take several years to learn their parents' language

effectively, and adults continue to hear and use new words or even languages throughout their lives. People can suffer a loss of voice when the vocal cords become inflamed or injured, or after experiencing psychological trauma (see INFLAMMATION). Speech therapists can help someone whose voice is not developing normally. Many conditions that affect the voice can be treated with either drugs or surgery. Computer-controlled speech synthesizers can be used by a person who cannot speak at all.

VOLATILE LIQUID (vŏl'ə tl lĭk'wĭd) A volatile liquid is one that has a high vapor pressure at normal temperatures. Vapor pressure is the force produced by vapor molecules as they escape during evaporation (see EVAPORATION; VAPOR; VAPOR PRESSURE). Because they have a high vapor pressure, volatile liquids evaporate quickly. Also, the boiling points of volatile liquids are not much higher than ordinary temperatures. Volatile liquids are used for cooling surfaces. For example, the compound chloroethane (ethyl chloride) is a very volatile liquid. Its boiling point is 54.5°F [12.5°C]. When it is sprayed onto the skin, it evaporates quickly. This cools the skin enough to anesthetize, or deaden the feeling in, it. Chloroethane is used as a local anesthetic.

See also ANESTHETIC; BOILING AND BOILING POINT.

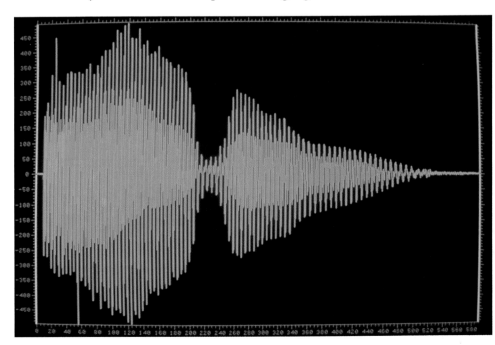

VOICE
A speech synthesizer produces the sounds of human speech. This computer graphics image shows the "shape" of the word *baby* produced on a speech synthesizer.

VOLCANO

A volcano is a vent, or opening, in the earth's surface through which lava, gases, and rocks erupt, or burst forth. Lava is magma (melted rock) that flows out of volcanoes (see EARTH; LAVA; MAGMA; VENT). *Volcano* also refers to the mountain or hill, called the cone, that forms around the vent. Volcanoes can be found on other heavenly bodies besides Earth, such as Venus.

A volcanic eruption is a dramatic sight. Volcanoes can also be very destructive, causing much damage and death when they erupt.

VOLCANIC FEATURES

Beneath a volcano, magma (molten rock) accumulates in a magma chamber. Great pressure forces the magma to the surface up a central vent, and the volcano erupts. Magma flows away as lava, and as it hardens, it builds up a volcanic cone. Other eruptions may take place along side vents and dikes. Sulfur lakes, mud pools, and geysers are often found near the volcano. After an eruption, the volcanic crater may collapse to form a caldera, which may fill with rainwater.

Formation of a volcano Geologists (scientists who study the earth) do not completely understand what causes volcanoes. Most scientists believe that great heat and pressure beneath the earth's surface cause rocks to melt, forming magma. The melting rocks release gas, which mixes with the magma. The formation of magma probably occurs about 50 to 100 mi. [80 to 160 km] below the earth's surface.

Magma is lighter than solid rock. As a result, the magma rises toward the surface. As it rises, it melts other rocks along the way. The magma rises until it

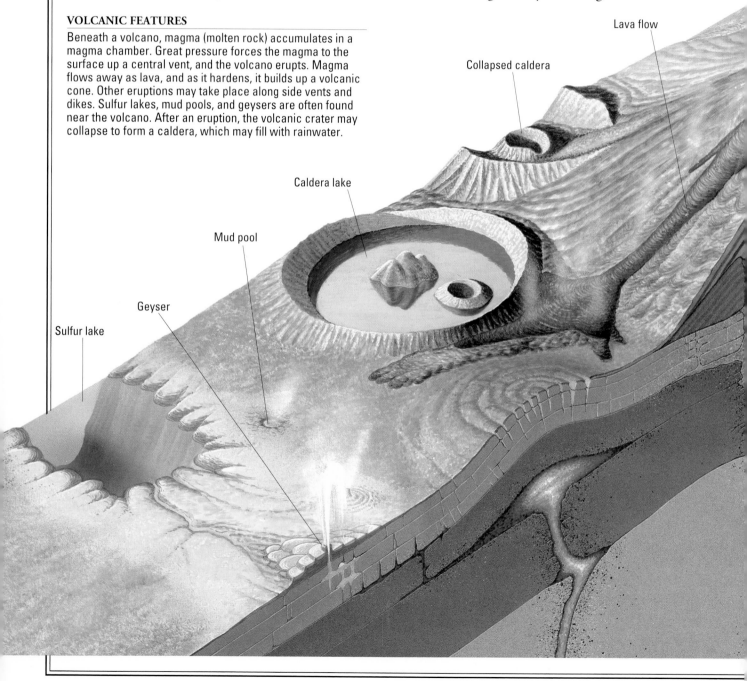

Lava flow

Collapsed caldera

Caldera lake

Mud pool

Geyser

Sulfur lake

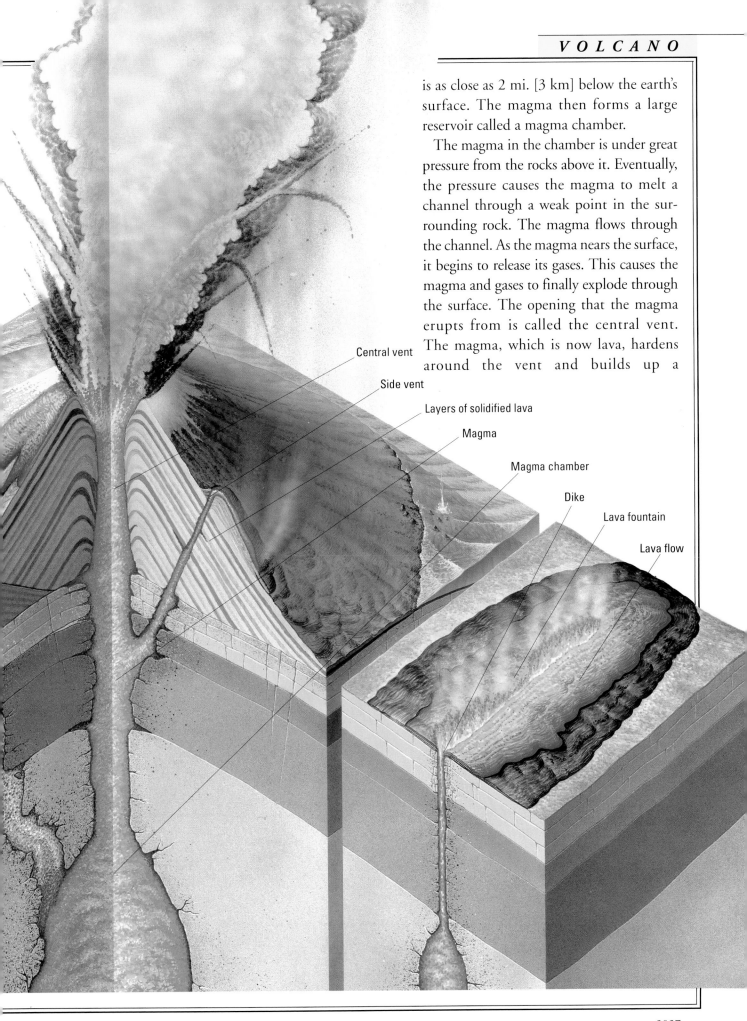

is as close as 2 mi. [3 km] below the earth's surface. The magma then forms a large reservoir called a magma chamber.

The magma in the chamber is under great pressure from the rocks above it. Eventually, the pressure causes the magma to melt a channel through a weak point in the surrounding rock. The magma flows through the channel. As the magma nears the surface, it begins to release its gases. This causes the magma and gases to finally explode through the surface. The opening that the magma erupts from is called the central vent. The magma, which is now lava, hardens around the vent and builds up a

Central vent

Side vent

Layers of solidified lava

Magma

Magma chamber

Dike

Lava fountain

Lava flow

INACTIVE VOLCANO

A volcano that stops erupting (above) is said to be inactive. Over a period of time, the soft rocks of the volcanic cone may be eroded away (above right), until eventually all that is left are the remains of the hard central plug (above, far right).

LAVA FOUNTAIN

When a volcano erupts through a vertical split in the rocks, called a dike, the lava shoots into the air as a spectacular fountain of molten rock (left).

volcanic mountain, or cone. Sometimes, magma melts smaller channels through the mountainside. Magma then flows out these secondary vents as well.

Volcanic material

The three main materials given off by a volcano are lava, gases, and pyroclastic rocks. Newly erupted lava may have a temperature of 2,012°F [1,100°C]. Lava is often classified according to its thickness. Very fluid lava quickly flows down from the vent. When it cools, it forms a smooth rock called *pahoehoe.* Thicker lava cools to form jagged rocks called *aa.* Lava may also harden into tunnels, tubes, and other interesting forms.

Gas belches out of an erupting volcano like smoke out of a chimney. Often, steam is formed from the heating of groundwater. The gas usually looks like black smoke.

Volcanoes also throw out many pyroclastic rocks, dust, and ash. Pyroclastic rocks are rocks that are formed from volcanic action. These rocks are often thrown high into the air during an eruption. The largest rocks are called volcanic bombs. Volcanic dust is made up of tiny particles with diameters less than 0.01 in. [0.25 mm]. This dust may be carried by the wind around the world, causing spectacular red sunsets. Volcanic ash is made up of particles with diameters less than 0.2 in. [0.5 cm]. Volcanic ash usually falls directly to the surface. Volcanic ash

preserves fossils well (see FOSSIL). Sometimes, the ash mixes with water to form a mudflow.

Kinds of volcanoes

Volcanoes are classified by the kind of lava they produce. There are two main kinds—basaltic lava and andesitic lava.

Basaltic lava is runny and flows easily. It flows for great distances before becoming solid. Volcanoes built up by basaltic lava are broad and shallow, and are sometimes called shield volcanoes. The magma that produces basaltic lava comes straight up from the earth's mantle, sometimes over hot spots, which are areas of high mantle activity, as in Hawaii, or along the oceanic ridges, as in Iceland.

Andesitic lava is richer in the mineral silica than basaltic lava is. The silica makes it stiffer and less runny. Volcanoes made from andesitic lava are tall and conical. Sometimes the lava hardens in the vent, and the volcano explodes as pressure is built up beneath it. The magma comes from remelted material in the earth's crust. Andesitic volcanoes are dangerous, such as the volcanoes of Mount Saint Helens in Washington or Mount Vesuvius in Italy.

Volcanoes used to be classified as active, dormant, or extinct. As it is difficult to tell if a volcano is actually extinct (it will never erupt again), or just dormant (it is liable to erupt at any time), volcanologists now classify volcanoes as either active or inactive.

Volcanology Volcanology is the study of volcanoes. Volcanologists study the origins, eruptions, and locations of volcanoes. There are about six hundred active volcanoes in the world. The chief area of volcanic activity is called the Ring of Fire. It lies around the Pacific Ocean. Other areas of volcanic activity include the central Mediterranean region, Iceland, the Great Rift Valley in eastern Africa, and Hawaii.

Scientific theories and observations since the 1500s helped form the current theory of volcanoes. Since the mid-1960s, geologists and other scientists have used the theory of plate tectonics to explain volcanic activity (see PLATE TECTONICS).

Plate tectonics says that the earth's crust is made up of about twenty plates that are constantly, but slowly, moving. When two plates move apart, a rift zone is formed. This happens in the mid-Atlantic ridge, which passes through Iceland. When the plates pull apart in rift zones, basaltic

magma bubbles up in order to patch the rift. This would explain the less violent flows of lava that occur in Iceland.

When two plates press against each other, one plate usually slides under the other in what is known as a subduction zone. The plate that slides down is melted, and the liquid rises through the plate above as andesitic magma and erupts at the surface. Certain things signal a volcanic eruption in subduction zones. There is usually a rise in temperature close to the volcano, gases coming from the vent, and earth tremors (shakings). An instrument called a tiltmeter is used to measure changes in the contours of a volcanic mountain. Today, volcanologists can even identify volcanic "hot spots" that appear on photographs made by weather satellites (see SATELLITE).

Even though forecasting volcanic eruptions is not always accurate, scientists have been more and more successful. The weather satellite *Nimbus II* produced information that indicated a coming eruption on the volcanic island Surtsey, near Iceland, a day before it erupted in 1973. In 1980,

CRATER LAKE

This crater lake formed when the crater of an inactive volcano in New Zealand collapsed and filled with rainwater.

MOUNT SAINT HELENS

Mount Saint Helens, a volcano in Washington, erupted in 1980. It threw dense clouds of smoke and ash into the atmosphere.

scientists knew in advance that the 40,000-year-old Mount Saint Helens in the state of Washington was about to erupt. Many lives were saved because people were asked to leave the area before the eruption. The eruption of Mount Saint Helens may have been the most closely studied violent eruption of all time. Photographs, measurements, and tests proved many theories. These theories will be useful in forecasting other volcanic eruptions.

The high cost of equipment, the lack of trained volcanologists, and the wide geographic scattering of volcanoes make forecasting difficult, however. Also, volcanoes must be studied over long periods of time to obtain useful information.

Volcanoes do serve useful purposes. They allow the release of energy that builds up between the earth's moving plates. They also help fertilize soil. People in Iceland heat their homes with steam from volcanoes.

See also ENERGY.

VOLE The vole is a small, stout rodent with short legs and tiny ears. Most voles have a body length of about 5 in. [13 cm]. Most voles have gray or brown fur. Voles are often named for the places in which they live. Several kinds of meadow voles are commonly found in North America. Voles may live in grassy fields or swamps. Some voles live near water. Others live in wooded areas or rocky, mountainous areas, often close to the snowline. Voles feed on grass, roots, and seeds and often make long tunnels just under the ground (see RODENT).

Voles are close relatives of lemmings. Voles have been responsible for damaging huge areas of meadowland in the United States.
See also LEMMING.

VOLE

Voles are found throughout the Northern Hemisphere. Pictured here are a meadow vole (top), drumming an alarm signal with its hind foot, and a taiga vole (bottom), standing on its hind legs to keep a watch out for danger.

VOLT The volt is an electrical unit. It measures the electrical potential difference between two points. Suppose that two points are at different electrical potentials. Then work has to be done to move an electric charge from one point to the other. If the size of the charge is one coulomb and the work done on it is one joule, then the potential difference between the two points is one volt (see COULOMB; ELECTRICITY; JOULE; POTENTIAL).

Small voltages are measured by instruments called potentiometers. They can measure voltages as small as a millionth of a volt. Larger voltages are measured by galvanometers or voltmeters. The volt is named after the Italian physicist Alessandro Volta.
See also ELECTROMOTIVE FORCE; GALVANOMETER; VOLTA, ALESSANDRO.

VOLTA, ALESSANDRO (1745–1827)

Alessandro Volta was an Italian physicist. He was born in Como, Italy. He became interested in electricity when he was quite young and later taught physics at the high school in Como. While he was there, he invented a machine called an electrophorus. This machine is used for building up a strong charge of static electricity. It was the basis of the capacitors that are in use today. Capacitors are devices that store electricity (see CAPACITOR AND CAPACITANCE; ELECTRICITY).

Volta's electrophorus made him famous. He became a university professor and continued his work with electricity. His most famous achievement was the invention of the electric battery (see BATTERY). This invention came out of research based on the discoveries of the Italian doctor Luigi Galvani (see GALVANI, LUIGI). Volta proved that the electric current that Galvani got from connecting two metal wires to a frog's leg muscle came from the metals. He went on to make an electric current from two metal plates in a salt solution. He improved this design to make what is called a voltaic pile. In 1801, he was invited to show this invention to the French Emperor Napoleon III. Volta was awarded many honors and medals for his work. The volt, the unit that measures the potential difference between two points, is named after him.

VOLTAGE REGULATOR Many electrical devices, such as radio receivers and electric motors, need an exact voltage to work properly. To keep the voltage at the desired value, these devices contain a voltage regulator. Some voltage regulators work automatically. Others are operated manually (by hand).

See also ELECTRICITY; VOLT.

VOLTMETER A voltmeter is an instrument that is used to measure the potential difference, or voltage, between two points. Most voltmeters are galvanometers with a large resistance in series with the coil.

See also GALVANOMETER; VOLT.

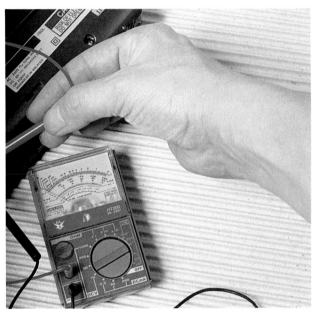

VOLTMETER
Voltmeters measure the voltage between two points.

VOLUME Volume is a measure of space. The space can be filled with a liquid, a solid, or a gas, or it can be a vacuum inside a container. The volume of a solid is measured in units such as cubic inches or cubic feet [cubic centimeters or cubic meters]. The volume of a liquid is measured in units such as fluid ounces, pints, or quarts [milliliters or liters]. The volume of a gas is not fixed unless it is enclosed in a container (see GAS; LIQUID; SOLID; VACUUM).

There are several ways to measure volume. For example, the volume of a rectangular or square object is found by multiplying the length by the width by the depth. The volume of a cylinder is found by multiplying the area of the base by the height. The area of the base is found by multiplying π (pi), which is equivalent to about 3.1416, by the square of the radius (see RADIUS). Liquids are measured by special devices that have a scale marked on them.

The volume of a container should not be confused with its capacity. Capacity is how much substance (usually a liquid) a container will hold, while its volume is how much space it occupies.

VOLVOX (vŏl′vŏks′) Volvox is a microscopic organism that contains chlorophyll and has a flagellum. Most scientists classify it as an alga or as a protozoan in the kingdom Protista. Because it contains chlorophyll, volvox is able to produce its own food by photosynthesis. Because it has a flagellum, volvox is able to move under its own power (see ALGAE; CELL; CHLOROPHYLL; FLAGELLUM; PHOTOSYNTHESIS; PROTOZOA).

Although volvox is basically a single-celled organism, the cells usually cluster together to form ball-shaped colonies of as many as sixty thousand cells. As each cell waves its flagellum, the colony rolls through the water. Some colonies produce smaller "daughter" colonies, which may break away from the parent colony. These daughter colonies then form new colonies of their own. Some colonies produce male and female gametes. These gametes combine to form a zygote, which stays in the

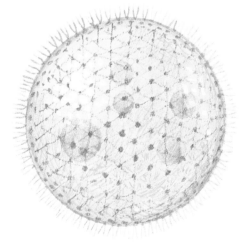

VOLVOX
A colony of single-celled volvox forms a ball that rolls through the water by waving its many flagella (plural of *flagellum*).

parent colony. When the parent colony dies, these zygotes are released and can form new colonies. The zygotes are thick walled and can survive unfavorable environmental conditions.

See also GAMETE; ZYGOTE.

VULCANIZATION (vŭl′kə nī za′shən) Vulcanization is the process of treating rubber to give it certain useful properties. In its natural state, rubber tends to become soft and sticky in warm weather. In cold weather, it tends to become brittle and to crack. Over the years, scientists tried to remove these undesirable properties. This was finally achieved by the American inventor Charles Goodyear in 1839. He discovered that the properties of rubber were improved if sulfur were added and the mixture heated. This process is called vulcanization. Vulcanized rubber is much tougher than natural rubber and can be used for many more purposes. The molecules of rubber are like very long chains (see MOLECULE). It is thought that during vulcanization, these chains are linked to each other by the sulfur atoms. This prevents the molecules from stretching, and the rubber becomes hard but not brittle.

See also RUBBER.

VULCANIZATION—Tires
The chief use of vulcanized rubber is for producing vehicle tires. Here a worker (left) is making a tire for a truck.

VULCANIZATION—Sulfur bridges
(1) A molecule of rubber takes the form of a zigzagged chain. When rubber is stretched, the chain straightens. When the stretched rubber is released, the molecule snaps back to its zigzag shape. This is why rubber is elastic. (2) Vulcanization links chains of rubber molecules with "bridges" formed by sulfur atoms, shown in yellow. As a result, the rubber becomes tougher and more useful.

VULTURE A vulture is a large bird found in the Americas that belongs to the family Cathartidae. Its head has no feathers. The bill of a vulture is hooked and powerful. A vulture eats dead animals. It uses its bill to tear the flesh off the bones. Very rarely, a vulture will kill and then eat an animal.

There are three species of vultures in North America. The turkey vulture, also known as a buzzard, grows to lengths of 25 in. [62.5 cm] and has a wingspan of 72 in. [180 cm]. It is found from southern Canada to the southern tip of South America. The slightly smaller black vulture ranges from the central United States to southern South America. The California condor, the largest land bird in North America, reaches lengths of 45 in. [112.5 cm] and may have a wingspan of 120 in. [300 cm].

The California condor had almost become extinct by the 1980s. The birds lived in a region popular with hunters, and they swallowed large amounts of lead pellets when they fed on carcasses (dead bodies) of animals that had been shot. In the mid-1980s, scientists took the remaining birds into captivity, where their number has been increasing. Some birds were returned to the wild in the mid-1990s, but the new habitat was not right. Ornithologists (scientists who study birds) continue to search for a suitable place to re-establish the California condor in the wild.

There are also birds called vultures in Europe, Africa, and Asia. However, these birds belong to the hawk family, Accipitridae.

See also ENDANGERED SPECIES; EXTINCTION; HAWK; SCAVENGER.

VULTURE

There are seven species of vulture in the family Cathartidae. Pictured here are (1) the king vulture, which lives in the rain forests of Central and South America; (2) the black vulture of North and South America; and (3) the California condor, an endangered species from the western United States.

W

WADER *Wader,* or *shorebird,* is a general term for a long-legged bird that spends much of its time in the shallow waters of marshes and seashores. Most waders also have long beaks. They use their beaks to probe the mud in search of worms and other small animals. Most waders nest far inland and migrate to the coasts in winter. Waders belong to

WADER

Waders have long legs and beaks adapted for the type of food they eat. Pictured here are (1) a jabiru stork from tropical America, (2) an African shoebill stork, which eats lungfish, and (3) a black-necked stilt, a type of shorebird.

several families, the largest of which is Scolopacidae. Its members include the curlew, redshank, ruff, sandpiper, snipe, turnstone, and woodcock. Other well-known waders are the storks, herons, avocets, and oyster catchers. The oyster catcher inserts its long, bladelike beak into a partly open bivalve, such as a clam, and scoops the animal from its shell.

See also AVOCET; BIRD; CURLEW; HERON; MIGRATION; STORK; TURNSTONE.

WAKSMAN, SELMAN ABRAHAM

(1888–1973) Selman Waksman was a Russian American microbiologist. He was born at Priluki in Russia and became a United States citizen in 1916. In 1939, Waksman was at Rutgers University in New Jersey when another scientist discovered a microorganism that lived in soil that could kill bacteria. Research was already underway to isolate penicillin. Waksman gave the general name *antibiotic* to penicillin and the soil microorganism. He then set out to find if there were other molds that produced antibiotic substances (see ANTIBIOTIC; BACTERIA; MICROORGANISM; MOLD; PENICILLIN).

Waksman discovered that a mold of the Streptomycete family could kill pathogens (organisms that cause disease). He extracted the pure antibiotic from the mold in 1943 and called it streptomycin. He was awarded the 1952 Nobel Prize for medicine and physiology for this work. Waksman gave the prize money to the research fund at Rutgers and continued with his work.

WALKINGSTICK
The walkingsticks, or stick insects, are slender insects belonging to the family Phasmidae. There are over 2,000 species. Their bodies look so much like sticks or twigs that these insects can hardly be seen as they eat leaves in trees and shrubs. Although some species have small wings, they rarely fly. Some species give off a foul-smelling liquid if threatened.

Most walkingsticks lay eggs that fall to the ground. These eggs look like seeds, so most are eaten by hungry animals. In some walkingstick species, there are few, if any, males. Their eggs develop by parthenogenesis (see PARTHENOGENESIS).

Although found in many of the warmer parts of the world, most walkingsticks live in the tropics. One tropical species, which is 13 in. [32 cm] long, is the longest of all living insects.

See also INSECT; CAMOUFLAGE; PROTECTIVE COLORATION.

through competition with dogs called dingoes and other animals introduced by humans, such as foxes. Other types are now endangered for the same reason. *See also* ENDANGERED SPECIES; EXTINCTION; KANGAROO; MARSUPIAL.

WALLABY

Wallabies are small kangaroos that live in Australia and New Guinea. Pictured here are a bridled nailtail wallaby from Australia (top) and a lesser forest wallaby from New Guinea (bottom).

WALKINGSTICK

Most walkingsticks live in tropical regions. The insect at the top is a South American species from Peru. The walkingstick at the bottom, measuring up to 10 in. [25 cm] long, is the largest in Australia.

WALLABY (wŏl′ə bē) The wallaby is a small kangaroo. It belongs to the group of mammals known as marsupials. The wallaby has long hind legs, small front legs, and a sturdy tail. When sitting in an upright position, the wallaby often uses its tail to lean on. There are many kinds of wallabies. The animals range from 1 to 3 ft. [30 to 90 cm] in length, not including the tail. *Bush kangaroo* is another name for the wallaby.

Wallabies live in various places, from open fields to dense forests. The animals are found in Australia and New Guinea, a large island to the north of Australia. Some species have become extinct

WALLACE, ALFRED RUSSEL (1823–1913) Alfred Russel Wallace was a British naturalist. He was born in Usk, Wales. He set off on an expedition to the Amazon River in South America in 1848. In 1854, he traveled to Australia and Asia.

On his travels, Wallace studied carefully the many different organisms he saw. He could see that there were major differences between animals from one area and another. He decided that the world could be divided into six areas in which the animals are very different. These areas are now called Wallace's Realms. They are the Palearctic, Nearctic, Neotropical, Ethiopian, Oriental, and Australasian regions.

Wallace worked out a theory of evolution at about the same time as another British naturalist, Charles Darwin. Both men agreed that natural selection was the key to evolution.

See also DARWIN, CHARLES; EVOLUTION; NATURAL SELECTION.

WALLEYE A walleye is a freshwater fish that belongs to the perch family, Percidae. It is usually brownish in color with a white belly, pointed snout, and many sharp teeth. The walleye averages between 13 to 20 in. [33 to 50 cm] in length. It feeds mostly on other fishes, though young walleyes eat insects. The species is found from the southeastern United States to the arctic circle. It is the most common fish in some parts of central Canada.

The walleye is a very popular game fish. The flesh is highly prized for food. The fish is called a walleye because its eyes are large and silvery. When the fish dies, the eyes become white.

See also FISH; PERCH.

WALLFLOWER The wallflowers are a group of perennial plants that belong to the genus *Cheiranthus* of the mustard family (see MUSTARD FAMILY; PERENNIAL PLANT). The common wallflower is a native of the Mediterranean region, where it grows on walls and cliffs. It has woody

stems up to about 2 ft. [60 cm] tall and spear-shaped leaves. The wild plant has bright yellow, fragrant flowers, but there are many cultivated varieties with a wide range of colors, from cream to deep red and purple.

WALNUT The walnut is a tree that bears one of the more popular nuts in the world. The tree belongs to the family Juglandaceae. Several types of walnut trees grow in the United States. The black walnut and white walnut, or butternut, are native to the eastern part of the country. The English, or

WALNUT

The English walnut, which grows in California and Oregon, forms a tall tree with spreading branches (top). Walnuts (bottom) are valued for their mild flavor.

WALLFLOWER

Wild wallflowers, originally from the Mediterranean region, have yellow flowers. Cultivated varieties have a wide range of colors.

Persian, walnut is grown in California and Oregon. The wood of black and English walnut trees is used to make fine furniture.

English walnut trees have gray bark, large compound leaves, and mild-flavored nuts (see LEAF; NUT). Black walnut trees are grown mainly for their dark brown, fine-grained wood. Black walnut trees are the largest of the walnuts and can grow 150 ft. [46 m] high.

The United States leads the world in the production of walnuts. The area around Stockton, California, is the center of the country's walnut industry.

See also TREE.

WALRUS The walrus is a mammal that lives in the Arctic Ocean, Atlantic Ocean, and Pacific Ocean. It is a type of large seal (see MAMMAL; SEAL). The walrus is the only seal with tusks. The walrus uses its two ivory tusks, which are actually upper canine teeth, to dig for shellfish, to climb on ice, and for defense (see TEETH). The tusks may grow as long as 39 in. [99 cm]. The animal's four feet are flattened into flippers. They help make the walrus a good swimmer.

An adult male walrus is larger than the adult female. Males grow to about 12 ft. [3.7 m] in length and weigh up to 3,000 lb. [1,400 kg]. The

WALRUS

The walrus is a type of large seal that usually lives in a herd. Walruses are the only seals with tusks, which they use in combat and to help pull themselves onto the ice.

baby, called a calf or pup, feeds on its mother's milk for about two years. Most walruses live in herds.

Walruses are hunted chiefly for their meat. Eskimos use the hides to make various things, such as small boats. Eskimos also use oil or fat from the walrus as fuel for heat and light.

WARBLER

Most of the species of wood warblers that live in North America migrate south for the winter.

WARBLER In the Americas, the warbler is a small bird that belongs to the family Parulidae. They are not related to the Old World warblers, which belong to the family Sylviidae. American warblers are usually called wood warblers. They chirp simple, melodious songs. They do not really "warble" their songs, as do the Old World warblers.

Of the 120 species of wood warblers, 55 live in North America. They feed mostly on insects and nectar (a sweet fluid found in many flowers) and range in length from 4 to 6 in. [10 to 15 cm]. Most of these warblers migrate south for the winter. Some migrate as far south as South America (see MIGRATION). They usually migrate at night in large flocks made up of several different species of warblers. Because most of the birds are dull in color at this time, it is often difficult to tell one species from another. By the time they return to their northern nesting areas in the spring, however, the males are usually brightly colored to help them attract mates. *See also* BIRD.

WARM-BLOODED ANIMAL A warm-blooded, or homeothermic, animal has a relatively

constant body temperature, regardless of the temperature around it. Mammals and birds are the only homeothermic animals (see BIRD; MAMMAL). In these animals, there is a balance between heat lost and heat produced. This balance is controlled by the part of the brain called the hypothalamus. Nerves are constantly sending the hypothalamus information about the temperature throughout the body. Based on this information, the hypothalamus makes the necessary adjustments (see BRAIN).

If the body is becoming overheated, for example, the blood flow to the skin increases. Perspiration increases as well. As a result, the body gives off more heat through the skin and cools down. Increased blood flow in the skin may make a person appear flushed, or red-skinned. If the body is becoming too cool, blood flow and perspiration

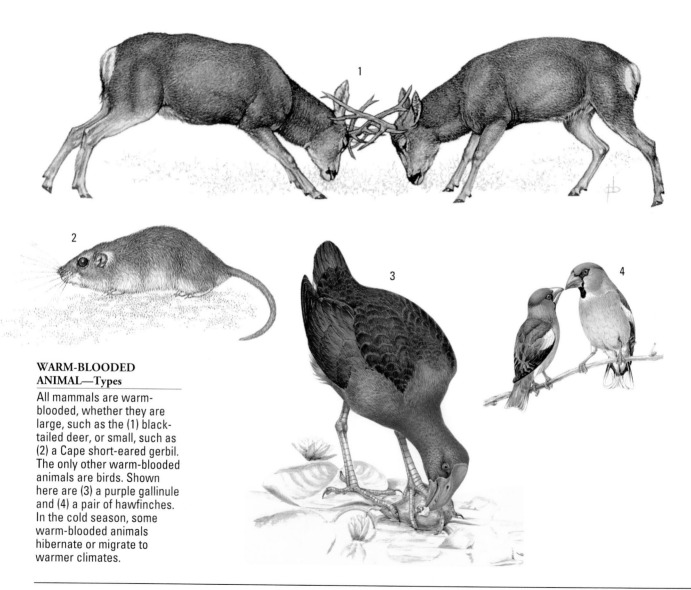

WARM-BLOODED ANIMAL—Types

All mammals are warm-blooded, whether they are large, such as the (1) black-tailed deer, or small, such as (2) a Cape short-eared gerbil. The only other warm-blooded animals are birds. Shown here are (3) a purple gallinule and (4) a pair of hawfinches. In the cold season, some warm-blooded animals hibernate or migrate to warmer climates.

**WARM-BLOODED
ANIMAL—Surroundings**
Even warm-blooded
animals can be affected by
the temperature of their
surroundings. This cat is
being warmed by the sun's
heat and the warm wall (red
arrows). But the cat is
cooled by radiating (giving
off) heat itself and by the
colder ground it is lying on
(blue arrows).

decrease, reducing heat loss. Tiny hairs on the skin may stand on end, trapping an insulating layer of air. Because body heat increases with muscular activity, shivering (involuntary muscle contractions) also occurs to help keep the body warm.

Each homeothermic animal has its own normal body temperature. For humans, it is 98.6°F [37°C], although it varies somewhat during the day. It is also affected by exercise or extremes of hot and cold weather. Some homeothermic animals hibernate (see HIBERNATION). During this time, an animal's body temperature drops to about the same temperature as its surroundings and all bodily activities slow down.

See also COLD-BLOODED ANIMAL; METABOLISM; TEMPERATURE, BODY.

WARM FRONT

A warm front is the surface along which an advancing warm air mass overtakes a retreating cold air mass. Warm air rides up over the cold.

Clouds form along the sloping boundary, with high cirrus clouds appearing first as the front approaches (see CLOUD; FRONT). The cirrus clouds are gradually replaced by cirrostratus clouds. The cirrostratus clouds become denser and lower as the warm front grows nearer.

Warm fronts generally move across the United States in an eastward direction. They bring about more gradual changes in weather than cold fronts do (see COLD FRONT). If moisture is in the air, the precipitation that occurs with a warm front is usually light but steady.

See also PRECIPITATION; WEATHER.

WARNING COLORATION

Warning coloration is used by an organism to tell other creatures that it is dangerous or undesirable. Warning coloration does not work unless the organism also has a bad taste or some other form of protection, such as a sting. Predators try to eat the animal once, but then quickly learn to leave it alone. An example of warning coloration is the bright pattern of red, black, and yellow colors on a poisonous coral snake. Other animals learn to recognize the snake by its unusual colors, and they stay away. Warning coloration is the opposite of camouflage (see CAMOUFLAGE). Camouflaged animals protect themselves by

WARNING COLORATION
The black, red, and yellow warning coloration of the eastern coral snake tells other creatures that it can be dangerous. The coral snake has a poisonous bite.

blending in with the area around them. An animal that shows warning coloration protects itself by making sure that every animal sees it—and stays away. *See also* MIMICRY; PROTECTIVE COLORATION.

WART HOG The wart hog is a wild African pig that is found from Ethiopia to South Africa. An adult wart hog stands about 30 in. [76 cm] tall at the shoulder and weighs up to 200 lb. [91 kg]. It has brown or gray skin and a long, coarse mane down the center of its back. The rest of its body has little or no hair. Wart hogs of both sexes have tusks that may reach 2 ft. [60 cm] in length. Between their tusks and their eyes, wart hogs have

WART HOG
Both male and female wart hogs have long tusks that they use as defensive weapons if they are cornered.

bulges, or warts, from which they get their name. The bulges are most obvious in the males.

Wart hogs travel in small groups. The female gives birth to as many as eight young at one time, although most have only 2 to 4 babies. Wart hogs prefer forests and grasslands and live in burrows, often using those built by other animals. They eat almost anything that is edible.

If provoked, wart hogs usually run away with their tails raised vertically. They may fight hard, however, using their large tusks as weapons. *See also* PIG.

WASP The wasp is a stinging insect related to bees and ants. The name is given to many kinds of insects belonging to the order Hymenoptera, but especially to the yellow jackets and hornets of the family Vespidae. Most wasps have slender bodies with a narrow waist and four wings. The bodies may have different colors. Yellow jackets have black bodies with bands of bright yellow. Other varieties of wasps are steel blue, black, or reddish. The mouths of wasps are fitted for chewing hard objects and lapping up liquids (see ANT; BEE; HORNET; INSECT).

Wasps give painful stings. However, they sting only when they are frightened or bothered. Only female wasps have stingers. The stingers are thin, pointed drills hidden in the rear tips of their abdomens (see ABDOMEN).

Yellow jackets and hornets live in colonies (groups) like those of bees and ants. There may be thousands of wasps in a colony. The colony is made up of three different kinds of wasps: queens (fertile females—that is, females who can reproduce), workers (sterile females—that is, females who cannot reproduce), and males. Each kind of wasp has a different job to do. Wasps that live together like this are called social wasps. Wasps that live alone are called solitary wasps.

Social wasps build their nests of wasp paper, which is made from dead wood and sometimes other plant fibers. The wasps chew this mixture into a pulp, using much saliva. When this pulp dries out, it becomes paper. Wasps mold this pulp into rows of cells (rooms) in which they raise their larvae, also called grubs. The nest itself may be located in several places—under a porch roof, attached to a rafter in an attic, in a hole in the ground, or hanging from the limb of a tree or shrub.

A wasp colony lasts only through the summer. Wasps do not store food, and most of them die in the fall. Young queens hibernate through the winter and form new colonies the following spring.

Solitary wasps live alone, and each female makes a small nest for her own offspring. The different kinds of solitary wasps have different kinds of nests. Potter wasps make dainty nests, often shaped like vases, out of mud and saliva. Mason wasps mix pebbles with mud and saliva and build nests on the surfaces of rocks in the open. Carpenter wasps tunnel into trees and posts. Earth-mining and digger wasps dig tunnels into the ground.

The adult wasps, both social and solitary, feed on nectar (a sweet juice from flowers) and fruit. Wasp grubs are fed on insects and spiders. Social wasps bring chewed-up insects for their grubs. Female solitary wasps feed their young with beetles, caterpillars, flies, and spiders. They catch and paralyze these organisms with their stingers and store them in their nests.

After laying one or more eggs in a nest, the female seals up the nest and goes away. Each larva hatches in a few days and finds the supply of food. Later, the larva spins a silken cocoon around itself and turns into a pupa. It may remain this way through the winter. The pupa turns into an adult wasp that gnaws its way out of the cocoon in the spring.

See also COCOON; METAMORPHOSIS.

WASP

Many wasps prey on other creatures, even other wasps. (1) A female ichneumon wasp uses her long ovipositor (egg-laying organ) to inject an egg into the larva of a wood wasp. (2) An American thread-waisted wasp drags a paralyzed larva back to its nest. (3) A solitary wasp stings the larva of a shieldbug. In each case, the prey becomes a source of food for the wasp's own offspring.

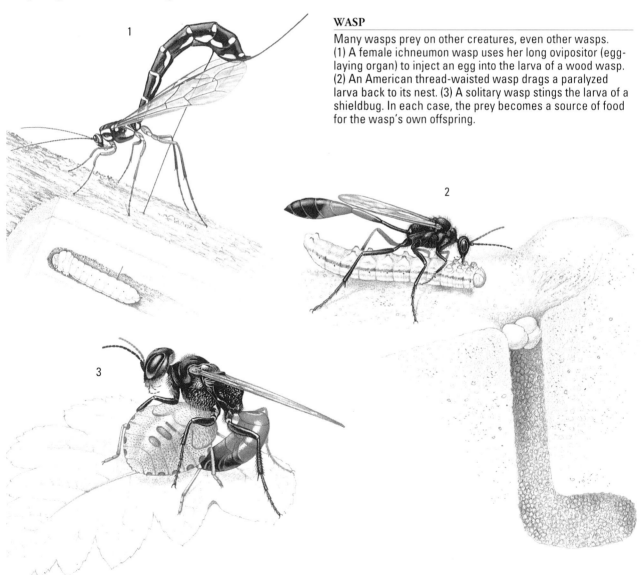

WASTE DISPOSAL

Waste disposal (wāst dĭ spō′zəl) is any method of removing wastes. Wastes are materials left over after something has been produced or used.

Most human activities produce wastes in gaseous, liquid, or solid form. The exhaust produced by automobiles or any other burning process is gaseous waste. Gaseous wastes often create air pollution (see POLLUTION). Steps are being taken to reduce the amount of gaseous wastes being released into the air. One of these steps is the use of unleaded fuels in automobiles. These fuels produce less pollution than fuels that contain lead. In addition, all states require cars to have devices that reduce the amount of pollution released in their exhaust (see CATALYTIC CONVERTER). Cars must also be checked periodically to determine the amount of pollution being released in their exhaust. Industries are also taking steps to reduce gaseous wastes. For example, many coal-burning electric-power plants are now burning low-sulfur coal, which produces less pollution. Also, electric-power plants have installed filters and scrubbers to remove pollutants from the smoke their plants release. Some plants are burning new kinds of fuels, such as old tires that have been shredded, that produce very small amounts of pollution.

Water and waste from drains and toilets is called sewage. Today in the United States, about 37.5 billion gallons [142 billion liters] of sewage per day

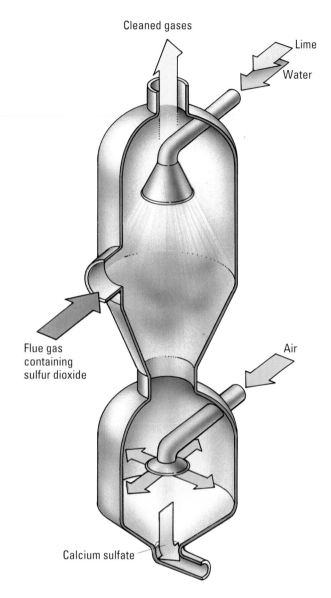

Cleaned gases

Lime

Water

Flue gas containing sulfur dioxide

Air

Calcium sulfate

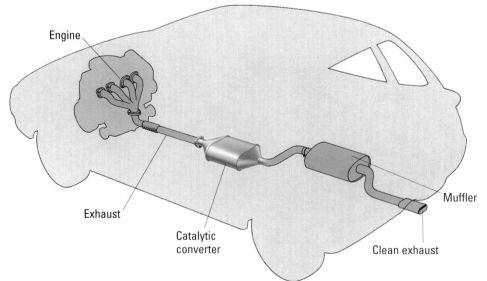

Engine

Exhaust

Catalytic converter

Muffler

Clean exhaust

CLEANING WASTE GASES

Waste gases from coal-burning electric-power plants and gasoline-powered automobiles can pollute the air. Flue gases from the boilers of power plants can be cleaned using a scrubber (above). The chief pollutant is sulfur dioxide, which is combined with lime to form solid calcium sulfate, or gypsum. In an automobile (left), a catalytic converter can change pollutant gases in the exhaust into harmless gases.

passes into the sewage system. The sewage travels to a sewage treatment plant, where it is processed and then emptied into a body of water. At the sewage treatment plant, the solid wastes are removed. Usually, harmful microorganisms are removed as well (see MICROORGANISM). Many treatment plants also remove dangerous chemicals and nutrients from the sewage. A problem with some sewage treatment is that not all the harmful substances are removed (see SEWAGE TREATMENT).

Solid wastes are often called garbage, rubbish, or trash. Aluminum cans, food scraps, leaves and grass clippings, glass containers, used newspapers and other paper products, plastic products, and scrap metal are solid wastes. Disposal of solid waste has become a huge problem because growing populations around the world have led to an increase in the amount of solid waste produced. The United States produces the most solid waste of any western country—over 1,600 lb. [720 kg] per person each year, on average. California produces the most solid waste of all the states—45 million tons [40.5 million metric tons] per year.

How solid waste is disposed of

About 10 percent of the solid waste in the United States is burned in machines called incinerators. A problem with this method is that the burning releases many pollutants into the air. Also, the leftover ash contains highly concentrated poisons. About 23 percent of the solid waste in the United States is recycled (see RECYCLING).

The other 67 percent of solid waste in the United States is collected and hauled to areas that have been specifically set aside for such a purpose. These areas are called landfills. Each day at landfills, the waste is packed under layers of soil. This is done to help the landfill cause as little damage as possible to the environment. For example, the soil prevents some odors from escaping and also helps keep animals from infesting the area. Some of the wastes then biodegrade (see BIODEGRADABILITY). Once filled, the landfill may be covered with soil for a final time. The land may then be used for such things as parks.

Landfills are not a problem-free solution, however.

Chemicals disposed of in landfills may seep into groundwater (see GROUNDWATER). This can be dangerous if the water is used for drinking. Recently, new laws have set strict standards for the building and operation of landfills. The standards

RECYCLING

Solid wastes can be reduced, and resources conserved, by recycling. Materials that can be reused in this way include aluminum from drinks cans (above) and waste paper (below).

LANDFILL
Most of the solid waste produced in the United States is collected and hauled to sanitary landfills.

are designed to reduce pollution. Many landfills are being closed because they do not meet the new requirements. In addition, many of the wastes disposed of in landfills, such as plastics, are not biodegradable. This means that landfills often fill up quickly. Because so many landfills are being closed, about half the states in the nation are expected to use up their existing landfill space by the year 2000. Although new landfills are being set up, the new environmental requirements mean that they are very expensive to build. It is also increasingly difficult to find places where residents do not object to having a new landfill site nearby.

Reducing solid waste Most scientists believe that the most important way to deal with the solid waste problem is to reduce the amount of waste produced in the first place. Ways to reduce wastes include buying recycled products, such as recycled paper products; avoiding buying products that cannot be recycled, such as disposable lighters, pens, and razors; using washable rather than disposable diapers, dishes, towels, and utensils; and reusing products, such as plastic bags and rechargeable batteries. There are many other ways to reduce wastes. For example, buying products, such as food or paper products, in bulk (large amounts) cuts down on extra packaging. Products purchased can be transported in reusable cloth bags instead of disposable plastic or paper bags. Also, food scraps and leaves and grass clippings can be turned into compost (see COMPOST).

Hazardous wastes Some gaseous, liquid, or solid wastes are very dangerous to humans and other organisms. These wastes, called hazardous wastes, may contaminate groundwater or soil. Those who come into contact with contaminated soil or water may develop cancer or other health problems (see CANCER). Hazardous wastes include certain chemicals, such as ammonia, drain cleaners, bleach, chlorine, and pesticides, from homes, farms, and factories; contaminated wastes from hospitals, such as used bandages and syringes; and radioactive wastes from nuclear power plants (see AMMONIA; CHLORINE; DIOXIN; NUCLEAR ENERGY; PESTICIDE; RADIOACTIVITY; TOXIC WASTE).

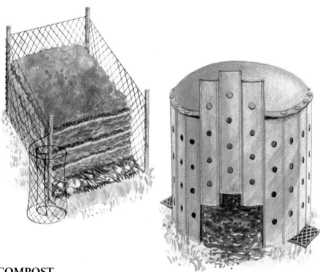

COMPOST
Kitchen waste and grass clippings can be put to good use by making them into compost. The compost can be contained in a homemade arrangement of poles and wire netting (above left) or in a commercial compost bin (above right).

For proper disposal of certain chemicals from homes, farms, and factories, some communities have permanent hazardous waste collection sites or special hazardous waste collection days. Hospital wastes are often burned to kill off microorganisms. In the past, hospital wastes were sometimes dumped into bodies of water and often washed up onshore. Scientists are now researching how to treat hospital wastes with the use of microwaves (see MICROWAVE). Microwaves would kill the microorganisms without releasing pollutants or producing poisonous ashes. At present, the only way to properly dispose of most radioactive wastes is to store them in radiation-proof containers. There is no permanent way to dispose of these wastes.

The dangers of hazardous wastes were not always known. For example, in the 1940s and 1950s, over 21,000 tons [19,047 metric tons] of hazardous wastes were buried at a site in the Love Canal neighborhood near Niagara Falls, New York. It was discovered in the 1970s and 1980s that some wastes were leaking from the site into surrounding soil and groundwater and other water supplies. This meant that homes that were built on the soil became contaminated. Also, people who drank the contaminated water developed cancer or other health problems. After much urging, especially from the people who lived in the neighborhood, the state of New York offered to buy the homes of anyone who chose to move out of the area. The state also paid for the cleanup of the wastes. In 1988, much of the area was declared safe to live in again, although some people still fear that the soil and water are contaminated. 🔬 PROJECT 70

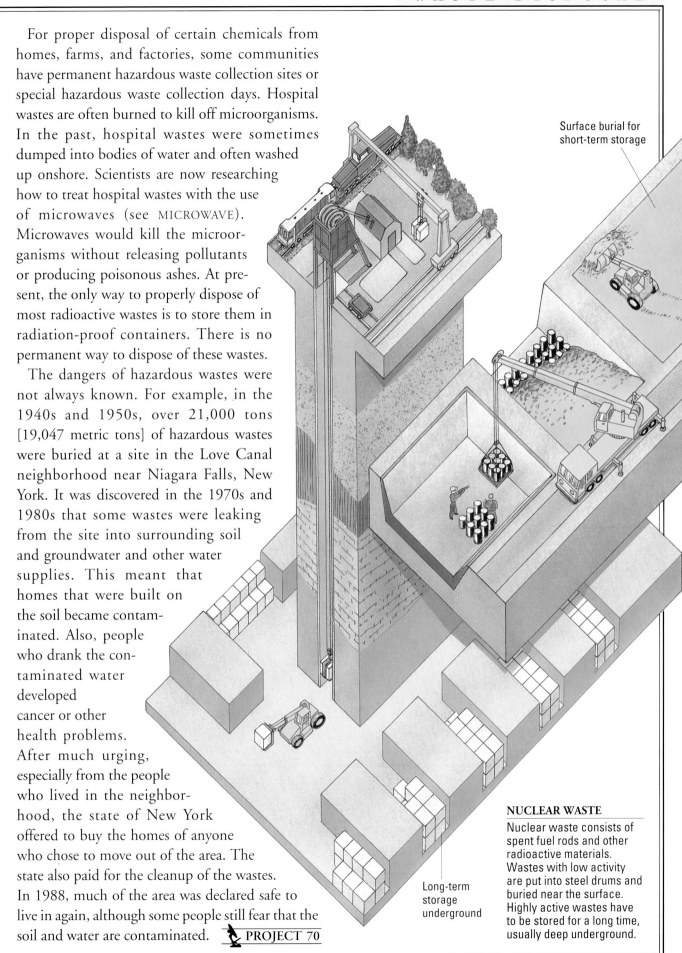

Surface burial for short-term storage

Long-term storage underground

NUCLEAR WASTE

Nuclear waste consists of spent fuel rods and other radioactive materials. Wastes with low activity are put into steel drums and buried near the surface. Highly active wastes have to be stored for a long time, usually deep underground.

WATER

Water is the colorless, tasteless substance that covers about 71 percent of the earth's surface. There are approximately 330 million cu. mi. [1.4 billion cu. km] of water on the earth. About 97 percent of the earth's water is salt water in the oceans. About 3 percent of the earth's water is fresh water. However, two-thirds of the earth's fresh water is frozen at the North and South poles. The other one-third may be found in lakes, rivers, streams, or underground in aquifers (see AQUIFER; GROUNDWATER).

estimate that the average American uses about 100 to 150 gallons [378.4 to 567.6 liters] of water daily. This may seem unbelievable, but consider these facts: It takes about 10 gallons [37.84 liters] for a person to brush his or her teeth if the water is left running. A three-minute shower uses about 45 gallons [170.28 liters] of water.

Plants, including food crops, depend on water for growth. Water dissolves minerals and other nutrients in the ground. The roots of plants draw this nutritious water from the soil (see MINERAL). In an area of sufficient rainfall, farmers do not have

WATERY FOODS
Some foods may contain more than 95 percent water. The watery foods shown here are (1) cucumber, (2) gherkin, (3) musk melon, (4) honeydew melon, and (5) watermelon.

FRESH WATER
Lakes and rivers supply most of the world's fresh water, although they contain less than 1 percent of the fresh water on the earth. Two-thirds of the fresh water is "locked" in the polar icecaps; the remainder is in aquifers.

Some water evaporates from the oceans and other large bodies of water. It returns to the earth as rain, snow, and other kinds of precipitation. This process is called the water cycle (see EVAPORATION; PRECIPITATION; WATER CYCLE).

Importance of water Water is necessary for all life on Earth. The human body contains about 65 percent water. Watermelons contain about 97 percent water. Most people could live a month or longer without food. However, a person will die after seven to ten days without water. Scientists

trouble having enough water for crops. In dry regions, however, water must be transported from a water source to the needy area. This process is called irrigation (see IRRIGATION).

Water is important for industry. Its main function is for cooling. Water is also used for cleaning, in air conditioning, and even as a raw material in such things as beverages and canned foods.

Water is an important source of power. Devices in a hydroelectric power plant convert the energy of flowing water into electricity (see ELECTRICITY; HYDROELECTRIC POWER).

Water is an important agent of erosion. Moving water, such as in a river, helps erode land. Water then carries this soil to the part of the river called the mouth to form a delta. Ocean waters are constantly eroding the coasts. Glaciers, which are huge masses of frozen water, erode land as they expand and retreat (see DELTA; EROSION; GLACIER).

Water is used by people for transportation. Before the invention of the airplane, the only way to cross oceans was in ships. Most trade with overseas countries is still done through shipping (see SHIPS AND SHIPBUILDING). People also use water for recreation, such as boating, fishing, and swimming.

Behavior of water The chemical formula for water is H_2O. This means that water consists of two hydrogen (H) atoms and one oxygen (O) atom. About 1 part in 4,500 parts of ordinary water is heavy water (see HEAVY WATER). Because water is a good solvent, most water also contains small amounts of dissolved substances, such as minerals (see SOLUTION AND SOLUBILITY).

Water is the only substance known that occurs naturally in three states of matter. The solid form

RIVER WATER
Rain falling in mountainous areas forms fast-flowing streams (1), which combine to form wider rivers (2). Eventually the river flows into the sea (3), adding to the water in the oceans.

of water is called ice. The gaseous form is called water vapor (see ICE; STATES OF MATTER; VAPOR).

At most temperatures on Earth, water occurs as a liquid. Liquid water weighs about 62.4 lb. per cu. ft. [1 kg per liter]. Water is liquid between 32°F [0°C] and 212°F [100°C]. At 32°F [0°C] or below, water freezes to become ice. Water expands when it freezes, so ice is less dense than liquid water (see DENSITY; FREEZING AND FREEZING POINT). This is why ice floats on the tops of lakes and ponds during the winter. Huge blocks of ice called icebergs float in the oceans near the North and South poles. Icebergs are sometimes dangerous to ships (see ICEBERG). Frozen water that occurs as precipitation may be called snow, sleet, or hail.

Water vapor is the gaseous form of water. When water reaches its boiling point of 212°F [100°C], it absorbs (takes in) heat when changing to steam. This absorbed heat is called latent heat. Steam can be used as a form of energy (see BOILING AND BOILING POINT; ENERGY; LATENT HEAT). Water vapor in the atmosphere is a major part of the weather. When water vapor condenses, it may fall as precipitation (see CONDENSATION).

Atmospheric pressure (the weight of air pressing

IRRIGATION

Water is essential for crops to grow. In dry regions of the world and during times of drought, water has to be transported to the fields. This process is called irrigation.

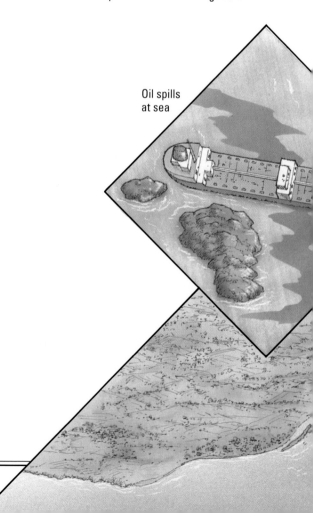

Oil spills at sea

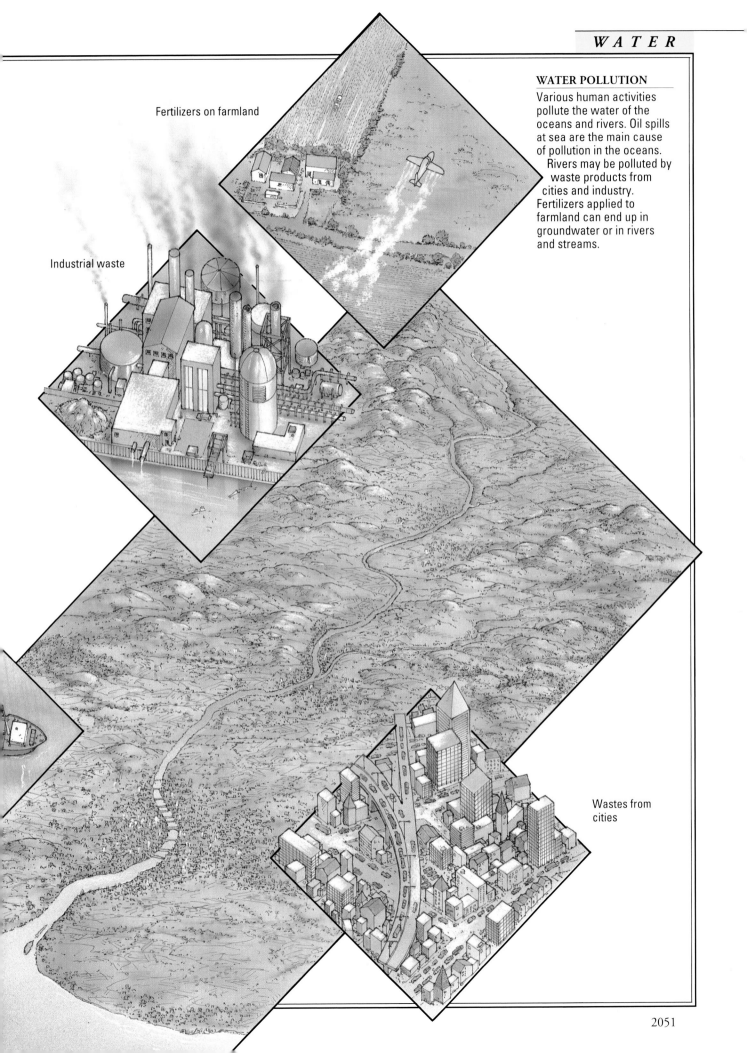

Fertilizers on farmland

Industrial waste

WATER POLLUTION

Various human activities pollute the water of the oceans and rivers. Oil spills at sea are the main cause of pollution in the oceans. Rivers may be polluted by waste products from cities and industry. Fertilizers applied to farmland can end up in groundwater or in rivers and streams.

Wastes from cities

2051

LAKES
Some fresh water from rivers accumulates in lakes. Many cities are located near lakes. Pictured here is Toronto, Canada, on the shores of Lake Ontario.

on the earth) affects the boiling point of water. For example, at sea level, water boils at the usual 212°F [100°C]. At an altitude of 1.8 mi. [3 km], where the atmospheric pressure is less, water boils at 194°F [90°C].

Water and humans Because people depend on water for life, they have developed complicated methods of purifying and transporting water (see WATER SUPPLY). Much progress has been made in the desalination (removal of salt) of ocean water to make it fit for humans to drink (see DESALINATION).

In spite of water's importance, much of it has been polluted by human activities (see POLLUTION). Pollution combined with overuse has led to dwindling supplies of water available for human use. Pollution comes from many sources. For example, farm chemicals, such as pesticides, may seep into groundwater or be washed by rain into rivers or streams (see PESTICIDE). Chemicals may leak from landfills, polluting groundwater (see WASTE DISPOSAL). Gasoline that leaks from underground storage tanks may also pollute groundwater. Sewage, or human waste, that is not properly treated may pollute water (see SEWAGE TREATMENT). The release of water that has been used in industry for cooling is another source of pollution. This water has become heated during the cooling process. When the hot water is released into a cooler body of water, it may harm many organisms there. A major source of water pollution is petroleum (oil). The oil may come from industries near coastlines that dump waste oil into the oceans; leaks from offshore drilling; or spilling of oil being transported by oil tankers (ships) (see TOXIC WASTE). **PROJECT 11, 58, 59**

ACTIVITY *How clean is rainwater?*

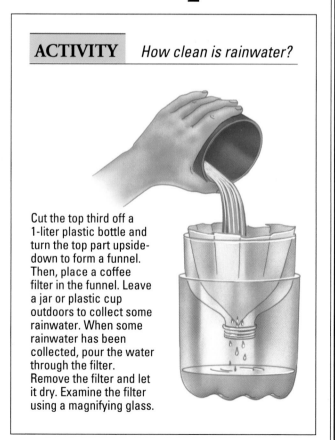

Cut the top third off a 1-liter plastic bottle and turn the top part upside-down to form a funnel. Then, place a coffee filter in the funnel. Leave a jar or plastic cup outdoors to collect some rainwater. When some rainwater has been collected, pour the water through the filter. Remove the filter and let it dry. Examine the filter using a magnifying glass.

WATERCRESS Watercress is a perennial, aquatic plant that belongs to the mustard family (see AQUATIC PLANT; PERENNIAL PLANT). It grows in cool streams and rivers in the Northern Hemisphere. Its stems and leaves taste like pepper and are a good source of vitamin C. They are often used in salads.

See also MUSTARD FAMILY; VITAMIN.

WATER CYCLE The water cycle is the journey of water from the oceans and other large bodies of water to the land and from the land back to the water bodies. The water cycle is also called the hydrologic cycle. The main driving forces of the water cycle are the sun's heat and gravity (see GRAVITY; SUN).

The heat of the sun evaporates water from the oceans. Air currents lift this evaporated water, or water vapor, into the atmosphere. As the air rises, it cools. When the air reaches its dew point, it becomes saturated. This means it can hold no more water. The water then condenses into droplets or ice crystals, forming a cloud. Precipitation, such as rain, sleet, or snow, falls from these clouds (see ATMOSPHERE; CLOUD; DEW POINT; EVAPORATION; PRECIPITATION; VAPOR).

Several things may happen to the precipitation if it falls on land. It may be absorbed, or taken in, by the soil. In this case, the water may be used by plants for nourishment, or it may move through the soil to form groundwater (see GROUNDWATER).

WATER CYCLE

Water vapor in clouds falls to the ground as precipitation such as rain or snow. The water may be absorbed by the land, it may form rivers and flow into lakes or oceans, or it may be used by plants and animals. Various processes return the water to the atmosphere. Evaporation returns water from bodies of water. Perspiration and breathing returns the water from animals. Transpiration returns the water from plants.

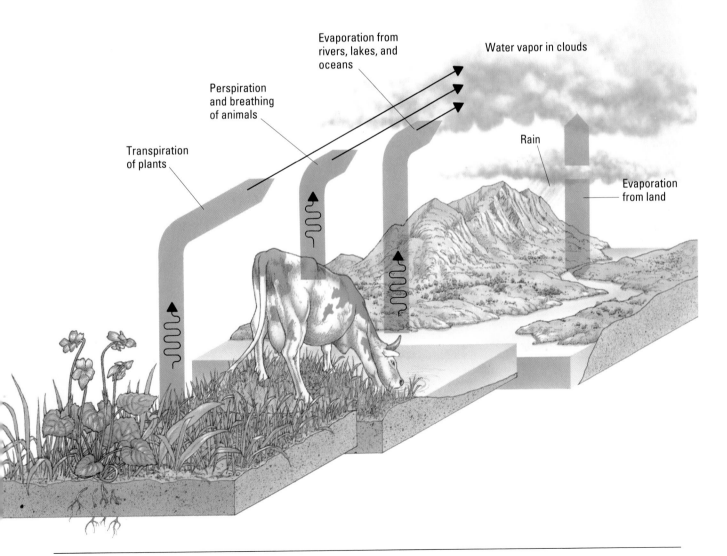

Transpiration of plants

Perspiration and breathing of animals

Evaporation from rivers, lakes, and oceans

Water vapor in clouds

Rain

Evaporation from land

Some of the precipitation may flow down slopes due to gravity. This water may find its way to a river or stream. Eventually, the river or stream empties into a larger body of water. It is then evaporated again.

The water that plants use is returned to the atmosphere by transpiration (see TRANSPIRATION). Animals return water through waste products, such as perspiration.

In cold areas, most precipitation falls as snow. In regions near the North or South pole or on high mountains, the snow may stay all year long. Eventually, the snow becomes ice. This mass of ice is called a glacier. About 2 percent of the earth's water is stored in glaciers (see GLACIER).

The water cycle is necessary for all life on Earth because it is constantly replenishing the earth's supply of fresh water.

See also WATER.

⚓ PROJECT 23

WATERFALL AND RAPIDS A waterfall is the falling of water from a higher level to a lower level. Waterfalls that have a small amount of water are called cascades. Waterfalls with a large amount of water are called cataracts. The terms *cascade* and *cataract* can also mean a series of waterfalls. Rapids are cataracts that have small, sloping falls.

WATERFALL AND RAPIDS

Waterfalls, such as Niagara Falls on the United States-Canadian border (right), are characteristic of rivers that are young in geologic time. The simplified cross section of the falls (below) shows how water flowing over limestone constantly undercuts the softer shale and sandstone beneath the limestone. From time to time, great slabs of limestone crash down, causing the falls gradually to retreat.

A river is constantly eroding, or cutting away, the layers of rock beneath it. Sometimes, an area of soft rock occurs downstream from an area of hard rock. The soft rock erodes much more quickly than the hard rock. After much erosion has occurred, a waterfall forms (see EROSION). Thus, the water flows downstream over the hard rock, then suddenly drops at the place of erosion, or waterfall. Often, soft rock lies underneath the hard rock at the ledge of the waterfall. This soft rock erodes because of the swirling water at the base of the waterfall. This is called undercutting. Undercutting is occurring at Niagara Falls in New York, where it is causing the cataract to recede (move back) by about 3.3 ft. [1 m] a year. Almost all waterfalls are cut back in this way. Eventually, the river runs a smooth course, and the waterfall no longer exists.

Waterfalls are often found in mountainous areas. They are also found in areas that have been eroded by glaciers.

See also GLACIER.

WATER FLEA Water fleas are small, aquatic crustaceans that belong to the genus *Daphnia.* Despite their name, they are not insects. A water flea is about 0.08 in. [2 mm] long and is almost completely enclosed by a thin, transparent (see-through) shell called a carapace. The animal swims through the water with a jerky motion, using its antennae as oars. Five pairs of leglike appendages are constantly moving, creating a flow of water through the carapace. The water brings a supply of oxygen and food to the tiny animal. The water flea's beating heart can be seen through the shell. Water fleas are sold as food for pet tropical fish.

See also ANTENNAE; CRUSTACEAN.

WATER LILY Water lilies are aquatic plants with large floating leaves. They are dicotyledons belonging to the family Nymphaeaceae (see AQUATIC PLANT; DICOTYLEDON). There are about 60 species, and they grow in both cool and hot

WATER LILY

Water lilies are common in cool and hot climates. They produce colorful flowers (top) and flat, rounded leaves (bottom). The leaves float on the surface of the water and the flowers grow just above the leaves.

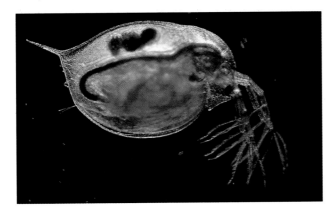

WATER FLEA

Despite being called a flea, a water flea is not an insect but a very small crustacean.

climates all over the world. Water lilies grow long stalks in the mud on the bottoms of lakes and ponds. The stalks support the leaves and flowers. The round or heart-shaped leaves float on the surface. The flowers either float on the surface or grow just above the leaves. The white-flowered water lily is the most common kind.

The giant water lily, found in the American tropics, is the largest water lily (see TROPIC). Its leaves often measure more than 6 ft. [2 m] across. They have upturned edges.

WATERSHED

A watershed is an elevation of land that causes streams on one side of it to flow in one direction and streams on the other side to flow in the opposite direction. These streams empty into different rivers. The rivers then empty into larger bodies of water, such as oceans. The Rocky Mountains in the United States are an example of a very high watershed. The Rocky Mountains separate the streams and rivers that flow into the Mississippi River from the streams and rivers that flow into the Pacific Ocean (see RIVER).

Watershed can also refer to that area of land that drains into a particular body of water. This area may be very large, such as the gently sloping hills that may extend several miles from a river.

WATER SOFTENING

Water softening is the process by which calcium and magnesium are removed from water (see CALCIUM; MAGNESIUM). Water containing these substances is called hard water. Hard water forms scales in pipes and does not easily dissolve soaps or detergents. Water softening is done in two main ways: the lime-soda process and the ion-exchange process.

The lime-soda process involves the addition of lime (calcium oxide) and soda ash (sodium carbonate) to hard water. These substances chemically combine with the magnesium and calcium in the hard water. The new chemical compounds, which do not dissolve in water, sink to the bottom of the water tank. The lime-soda process reduces the amount of magnesium and calcium in the water to about fifty parts per million.

The ion-exchange process reduces the amount of calcium and magnesium to about one part per million. This process involves passing water through a tank filled with grains of zeolite. As the water passes through, the sodium ions of the zeolite are exchanged for the magnesium and calcium ions in the water (see IONS AND IONIZATION). When most of the zeolite's sodium has been replaced by calcium and magnesium, a strong salt (sodium chloride) solution is flushed through the system. This salt solution removes the calcium and magnesium from the zeolite and replaces them with sodium. Now the zeolite can continue to soften the water.

See also WATER.

WATER SUPPLY

A water supply is the amount of readily available pure water in a specific area (see WATER). The water supply of an area depends mainly on its precipitation. Much of the Americas, Europe, central Africa, the eastern coast of Asia, and the coasts of Australia receive adequate precipitation. Other areas, such as northern Africa, central Asia, central Australia, parts of the western United States, the western coast of South America, and the Middle East, receive little precipitation (see PRECIPITATION).

In the United States, most households receive their water from public water systems. The water is usually drawn from rivers, lakes, or reservoirs, which are continually resupplied by precipitation (see RESERVOIR). Water from these sources must be purified—made fit to drink—by a complex series of treatments. Some people, especially those who live out of the reach of public water systems, get their water from groundwater. Groundwater is pumped to the surface through wells (see GROUNDWATER; WELL).

In many cities, the first step in water purification is pumping water from its source to a water treatment plant. At the plant, the water goes through a treatment process called coagulation. In coagulation, certain chemicals, such as alum, are added to the water (see ALUM). Suspended (undissolved) impurities in the water gather on the alum molecules to form substances called flocs (see MOLECULE). The water is then passed through a settling

tank. In the tank, the flocs fall to the bottom and are removed.

Not all the impurities in the water form flocs. Therefore, a second treatment called sand filtration is needed. In sand filtration, the water is filtered through a large concrete tank, which has a thick layer of fine sand on the bottom. The sand acts like a screen. Most of the impurities are removed in this step, though some microorganisms that cause disease may remain (see MICROORGANISM). To kill those microorganisms, the water undergoes another treatment such as chlorination. Chlorination is just one of the many disinfection treatments used to purify water. Chlorination involves the bubbling of chlorine gas, fluorine, and other chemicals through the water. Very low amounts of chlorine are enough to kill almost all of the microorganisms. Some microorganisms may remain, but not enough to cause disease (see CHLORINE).

The final step in water purification involves testing the water to see how acidic or basic it is. If it is too acidic or basic, the water is then neutralized (see ACID; BASE; NEUTRALIZATION). If the water is hard

WATER SUPPLY
Most water for homes and industry is obtained from reservoirs, which collect river water behind dams.

(that is, it contains large amounts of dissolved minerals such as calcium or magnesium), this also may be corrected at the plant. More often, however, hard water is treated in homes and other buildings in a process called water softening (see WATER SOFTENING).

From the water treatment plant, the water may be pumped to storage facilities, such as water towers. The water is then pumped to homes, offices, and factories in the community.

In the last ten years, there has been a growing concern that water treatment plants may not be purifying water enough. This is because conventional water treatment methods may not be able to remove certain kinds of pollutants (see POLLUTION). These pollutants include chemicals from agriculture; chemicals that have leaked from landfills; gasoline that has leaked from underground gasoline storage tanks; and petroleum (oil) that has leaked from offshore drills or spilled from tankers (ships).

Another major concern of recent years is that water supplies are dwindling. One of the reasons for dwindling water supplies is overuse by heavily populated communities and by farmers. Overuse causes another problem in coastal communities. When groundwater is drained, salt water from the oceans seeps in and replaces the water. The salt water contaminates the remaining fresh groundwater. Dwindling water supplies have prompted the use of "gray water" in some communities in the United States. Gray water is water that has been used for such purposes as washing dishes. Instead of passing to the sewage system, it passes to a special tank in the home. Before reaching the tank, however, the gray water passes through a series of filters. The filters clean the water enough so that it can be used for such purposes as watering the lawn or garden.
See also SEWAGE TREATMENT.　🔬 PROJECT 9, 17

WATER TABLE The water table is the depth below which the ground is saturated with water. Ground that is saturated cannot hold any more

water. When rain falls on land, some of it filters through the layer of soil called the zone of aeration until it reaches the zone of saturation. The top layer of the zone of saturation is called the water table. The water table is usually less than 100 ft. [30 m] beneath the surface. The water table roughly follows the bend of the land above it. The water table rises and falls according to the amount of precipitation. The lowest depth that the water table ever reaches is called the permanent water table.
See also GROUNDWATER; PRECIPITATION.

WATSON, JAMES DEWEY (1928–) James Watson is an American biochemist (see BIOCHEMISTRY). He was born in Chicago, Illinois. He graduated from the University of Chicago at the age of nineteen. In 1951, he went to England and worked with the scientist Francis Crick (see CRICK, FRANCIS HARRY COMPTON). There, the two scientists discovered the double-helix structure of DNA using measurements done by the British scientist Maurice Wilkins. DNA is the nucleic acid that is the

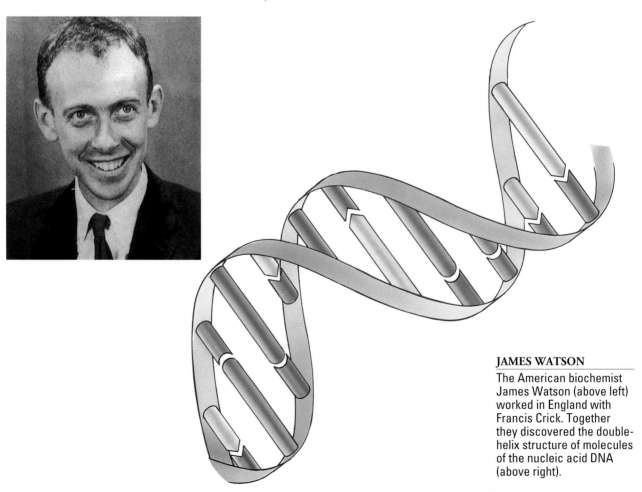

JAMES WATSON
The American biochemist James Watson (above left) worked in England with Francis Crick. Together they discovered the double-helix structure of molecules of the nucleic acid DNA (above right).

chemical basis of heredity (see DNA; HEREDITY). In 1953, Watson and Crick built a model of the DNA molecule that showed how the molecule reproduces itself during cell division. The model resembles a twisted ladder. It is called the Watson-Crick model.

For this discovery, Watson shared the 1962 Nobel Prize for medicine and physiology with Crick and Wilkins.

See also CHROMOSOME; GENE; GENETICS.

WATT The watt is a unit of power. Power is the rate of doing work (see POWER). A watt can be used to measure mechanical power or electrical power. In measuring mechanical power, if the work done is equal to one joule and it takes one second, then the power is equal to one watt (see JOULE). In measuring electricity, the power in watts is equal to the current in amperes multiplied by the voltage (see AMPERE; CURRENT, ELECTRIC; ELECTRICITY; VOLT). A thousand watts is called a kilowatt. A million watts is called a megawatt.

The amount of electrical energy that an appliance uses in a given period of time is measured in kilowatt-hours. A kilowatt-hour is determined by multiplying the appliance's power expressed in kilowatts by the length of time the appliance is operated expressed in hours. For example, a 1-kilowatt hair dryer that is operated for 1 hour uses 1 kilowatt-hour of electricity. If that same hair dryer were used for ten minutes, which is one-sixth of an hour, it would use 0.17 kilowatt-hours of electricity. The watt is named after the Scottish engineer James Watt (see WATT, JAMES). **PROJECT 34**

WATT, JAMES (1736–1819) James Watt was a Scottish engineer. He was born at Greenock, Scotland, and was taught at home by his mother. Watt traveled to London when he was eighteen to serve an apprenticeship as a mathematical instrument maker. After he completed the apprenticeship, he went back to Scotland and worked at the University of Glasgow as an instrument maker.

While at the university, Watt was asked to repair a model of a certain type of steam engine called a Newcomen steam engine (see STEAM ENGINE).

JAMES WATT
James Watt, a Scottish engineer, is best known for improvements he made to the design of early steam engines. The scientific unit of power, the watt, is named in his honor.

Watt became famous by improving this steam engine. In the Newcomen engine, a device called a piston, which was located inside a cylinder, was pushed up by the pressure of steam from a boiler below. The steam was then cooled by a jet of water sprayed into the cylinder. The cooled steam condensed, creating a vacuum (see CONDENSATION; VACUUM). The vacuum pulled the piston down again. In the Newcomen steam engine, the cylinder was repeatedly being heated and cooled, causing heat to be wasted. Watt improved the engine by having a piston move inside a cylinder that had two side openings, called ports. Steam was fed first through one port and then the other. This caused the piston to move from side to side. In Watt's engine, there was no need to cool the cylinder to create a vacuum, so no heat was wasted. Watt's steam engines were so improved that he is often credited with inventing the first steam engine. He went on to build many more engines, continually making improvements. Another invention of Watt's was a device to regulate engine speed.

Watt also introduced a way of measuring the power of engines by comparing them with the power of a horse. He decided that a horse could raise a weight of 150 lb. [68 kg] by 4 ft. [1.2 m] in a second. Watt called this amount of power one horsepower. Horsepower is still used as a unit for measuring the power of engines. However, it is the scientific unit of power, the watt, that is named in honor of him. One horsepower is equal to about 746 watts.

See also WATT.

WAVE

A wave is a disturbance that carries energy from one place to another. Waves can carry energy through gases, liquids, solids, and vacuums (see VACUUM).

A wave in water is one of the most familiar kinds of waves. Wind blowing across the ocean causes surface waves, which have crests and troughs. A crest is the top of a wave. A trough is the bottom. The strength of a wave is often measured by its amplitude, which is the distance between the undisturbed position to the top of the crest or to the bottom of the trough (see AMPLITUDE). The stronger the wind blows, the higher the crests and the deeper the troughs will be on the water's surface. There are also waves moving beneath the surface of the water.

There are many other kinds of waves. A person beating a drum or blowing a trumpet causes vibrations in the air called sound waves (see SOUND). Light travels as electromagnetic waves (see ELECTROMAGNETIC RADIATION). Earthquakes cause seismic waves. A bullet shot from a high-powered rifle produces compressional waves. Bomb blasts produce shock waves (see SHOCK WAVE). Boats also produce a type of shock wave called a bow wave. The V-shaped wave pattern of a bow wave appears to be dragged along behind the boat. However, the waves are actually spreading in the opposite direction.

Waves have mechanical properties that can be observed and measured. When a wave moves through a medium, two things can be observed: the movement of the wave and the movement of the medium. Descriptions of waves take into account such properties as wavelength, velocity, the density of the medium, and other physical factors related to space and time (see DENSITY; VELOCITY).

Huygens's principle
When a stone is dropped into still water, a ring of waves moves away from the point of disturbance. The ring grows larger and larger. Any short part of the wave front tends to form a straight line. If the straight line of the wave passes through an opening in a barrier, the wave coming out the other side does not form a straight line. Instead, the wave spreads out in a curved line

WATER WAVES

When waves move across the surface of water, the water does not move along with the wave. The body of water moves up and down as the wave passes.

again. This changing of a straight wave line into a curved line is called diffraction (see DIFFRACTION).

Christiaan Huygens was a Dutch astronomer, mathematician, and physicist. In 1690, he proposed a principle, now named Huygens's principle, which has been important to understanding waves. Huygens proposed that each point of an advancing wave is in fact the center of a fresh disturbance and the source of new waves. For example, if two rooms are connected by an open doorway, and a person sounds a trumpet in a remote corner of one room, a person standing in any part of the other room will hear the trumpet sounds coming from the doorway. The vibrating air in the doorway is the source of sound waves that enlarge in all directions through the second room.

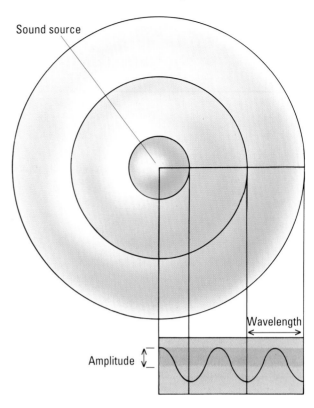

SOUND WAVES

Sound waves spread out from their source like ripples on the surface of a pond (above). The crests of the waves are regions of higher air pressure, and the troughs are regions of lower pressure. The distance between crests and crests, or troughs and troughs, is the wavelength. Amplitude (the height of the wave) corresponds to sound intensity.

Wavelength and frequency A wave is commonly referred to in terms of its wavelength or its frequency. Wavelength is the distance between two corresponding points on two consecutive waves. For example, wavelength may be measured from crest to crest or from trough to trough. The frequency of a wave is the number of cycles per second. Frequency is measured in units called hertz. High frequencies have short wavelengths. Low frequencies have long wavelengths (see FREQUENCY; HERTZ; WAVELENGTH).

Interference Interference occurs when two waves having about the same wavelength meet (see INTERFERENCE). They either combine to reinforce each other, or they cancel each other out. If the crests of two waves coincide, the wave at that point becomes stronger. The amplitude of the wave formed is the sum of each wave's individual

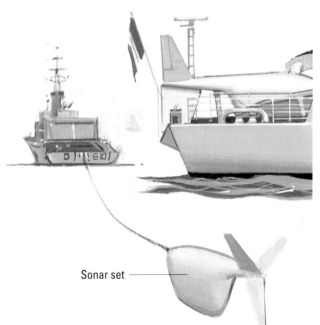

ULTRASONIC WAVES

A naval sonar set is towed behind a ship. Sonar sets send out and detect echoes of ultrasonic waves, which are sound waves that are too high in frequency for humans to hear.

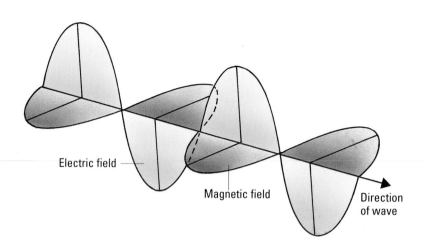

LIGHT WAVES
Light waves have electric and magnetic fields that move at right angles to each other in the direction of the wave.

Electric field

Magnetic field

Direction of wave

amplitude. This is called constructive interference. However, if the crest of one wave meets the trough of another wave, the two waves cancel each other out. This is called destructive interference.

When two waves of the same wavelength, velocity, and amplitude travel from opposite directions through the same medium, they combine to produce a standing wave (see STANDING WAVE). A standing wave is a wavelike disturbance that does not visibly move through the medium. Nodes are points along the medium that have the least amount of disturbance, or no disturbance at all (see NODE). Halfway between the nodes are points called antinodes. At the antinodes, the amplitude of the disturbance is twice the amplitude of the two separate waves combined.

Standing waves are created when the string of a musical instrument is plucked. A guitar string, for example, can vibrate with antinodes at each end when struck. This mode of vibration produces the fundamental, or main, note of the string. It is also called the first harmonic (see HARMONICS). The string can also vibrate in halves, with a node at the center as well as the ends. This vibration produces a higher-pitched note and is called the second harmonic.

Wave motion applications Wave motion is applied to the construction of supersonic aircraft, wind tunnels, and rocket combustion. Radio and television stations transmit programs on precisely measured wave frequencies. Artificially generated seismic waves are used in prospecting for natural

gas and petroleum (see PROSPECTING; RADIO; ROCKET; SUPERSONIC FLIGHT; TELEVISION). Ultrasonic waves are used in special surgical procedures instead of a scalpel (knife). X-ray waves can detect tumors and are used for the treatment of certain cancers (see ULTRASOUND; X RAY). Ocean wave motions are applied in the building of ships and submarines. Sonar systems are designed to detect objects under the water using sound waves (see SONAR). Knowledge of sound waves and harmonics is applied to the building and tuning of pianos, organs, and other musical instruments. Photographic equipment operates in response to controlled light wavelengths (see PHOTOGRAPHY).

See also LONGITUDINAL WAVE; TRANSVERSE WAVE.

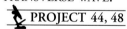 **PROJECT 44, 48**

ACTIVITY   *How to make waves*

Tie one end of a rope to a door handle. Make sure the door is closed. Now move the free end of the rope up and down rapidly. Waves will travel along the rope toward the door. The faster you move the rope, the shorter the wavelength of the waves.

WAX Wax is a solid, fatty substance that is widely used as a protective covering for many surfaces. It is also used to make candles and polishes. Wax is solid at room temperature but softens and becomes sticky when heated.

There are three kinds of wax: mineral, animal, and vegetable (plant). Mineral wax comes from petroleum. It resists moisture and chemicals and has no odor. It is used on milk cartons, on paper, and in polishes for automobiles, floors, and furniture. Animal wax, such as the wax produced by bees, is used to make candles and other products. Many plants have a natural wax that protects them from heat and moisture. Carnuba, the hardest wax obtained from plants, is an important part of automobile wax and other polishes.

WAXWING

The Bohemian waxwing (top) catches insects while flying through the air. Like the cedar waxwing (bottom), it gets its name from the waxlike tips of its wing feathers.

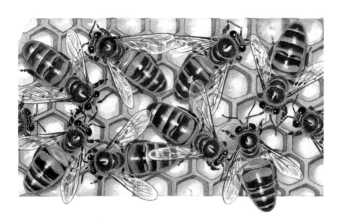

WAX

Beeswax is produced by bees (top) to make honeycombs in which larvae grow. Wax is used to make candles (left).

WAXWING A waxwing is a bird that belongs to the family Bombycillidae. It is a mostly brown bird, with white, black, and yellow feathers on its wings. The wings also have feathers with waxlike red tips, for which the bird is named. A waxwing has a crest (pointed feathers on top of its head) similar to that of a cardinal (see CARDINAL). The bird grows to 5 to 6 in. [13 to 15 cm] in length.

There are two species of waxwings in North America. The Bohemian waxwing is found in the northwestern part of the continent. The cedar waxwing lives throughout most of southern Canada, the United States, and Mexico. Both species eat berries and insects and travel in large flocks.

See also BIRD.

WEAK NUCLEAR FORCE The weak nuclear force is one of two forces that act inside the atomic nucleus (see NUCLEUS). The other nuclear force is called the strong nuclear force. Both nuclear forces are short-range forces. Their effects cannot be felt outside the nucleus. The weak nuclear force is 10,000 billion times weaker than

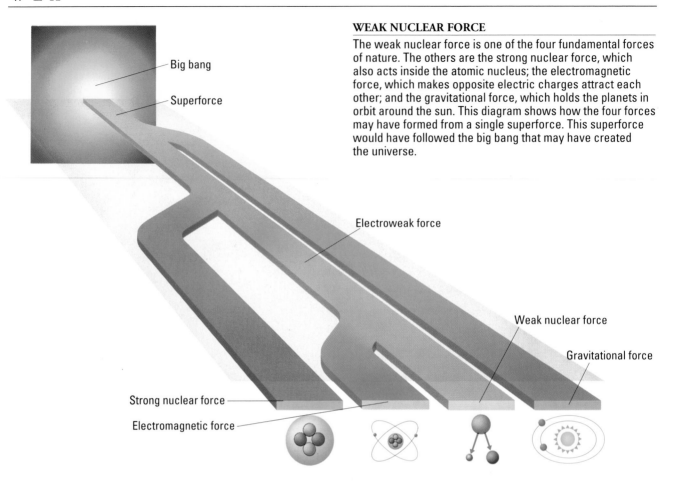

WEAK NUCLEAR FORCE

The weak nuclear force is one of the four fundamental forces of nature. The others are the strong nuclear force, which also acts inside the atomic nucleus; the electromagnetic force, which makes opposite electric charges attract each other; and the gravitational force, which holds the planets in orbit around the sun. This diagram shows how the four forces may have formed from a single superforce. This superforce would have followed the big bang that may have created the universe.

Labels on diagram: Big bang, Superforce, Electroweak force, Weak nuclear force, Gravitational force, Strong nuclear force, Electromagnetic force

the strong nuclear force. It is 100 billion times weaker than electrical and magnetic forces encountered in everyday life. Nevertheless, the weak force is strong enough to disrupt the nuclei of some atoms, causing them to break up (decay) (see ATOM; RADIATION; RADIOACTIVITY). This decay process produces heat and energy (see ENERGY). Inside the sun, the breaking up of nuclei by the weak force helps produce the energy that makes the sun shine.

WEASEL The weasel is a small, furry mammal that belongs to the family Mustelidae. The most widespread American species is the common long-tailed weasel (see MAMMAL).

The common long-tailed weasel is 12 to 18 in. [30 to 46 cm] in length and weighs up to 12 oz. [340 g]. It has a long, slender body covered with brown fur on the upper parts and white or yellow fur on the underparts. The fur of weasels that live in cold climates turns white in winter. Weasels have a sharp sense of smell and are excellent hunters. They eat voles, mice, squirrels, and other rodents, as well as birds and eggs. The weasel's slim body enables it to

squeeze through narrow openings when pursuing its prey. Weasels live under rock piles and tree stumps. They are active mainly at night (see NOCTURNAL BEHAVIOR). Their main enemy is the owl.

WEASEL

Weasels have long, slim bodies. Pictured here are the common long-tailed weasel of North America (top), the Patagonian weasel of South America (center), and the North African banded weasel (bottom).

Weather is the daily changes in the state of the earth's atmosphere. The study of the weather and the atmosphere is called meteorology. The scientists who study meteorology are called meteorologists. The typical weather for an area over a long period of time is called its climate. For example, the northeastern region of the United States has a continental moist climate. This type of climate has four distinct seasons, a wide range in temperatures, and plenty of precipitation (see ATMOSPHERE; CLIMATE; METEOROLOGY; PRECIPITATION).

Causes of weather One of the most important causes of weather is the amount of heat from the sun that a region gets. The tilt of the earth affects this. The sun's rays are less direct at high latitudes than at low latitudes (see EARTH; LATITUDE AND LONGITUDE). This means that cold air masses develop in the far north and far south, while warm air masses develop near the equator. The earth's atmosphere is constantly mixing air in an attempt to even out the temperature and pressure. Thus, the warm air masses meet the cold air masses between the equator and the poles. The boundary between the cold air and warm air is called the polar front (see AIR MASS; POLAR FRONT).

In the Northern Hemisphere, the polar front moves south during the winter and north during the summer. Movements of the polar front are mainly determined by strong winds high in the

SUN'S HEAT

The long-term weather pattern of a region and seasonal changes in the weather depend mainly on the amount of heat the region gets from the sun (above). In summer, the weather is warm and any precipitation falls as rain. In winter in higher latitudes, the weather is cold and precipitation falls as snow (left).

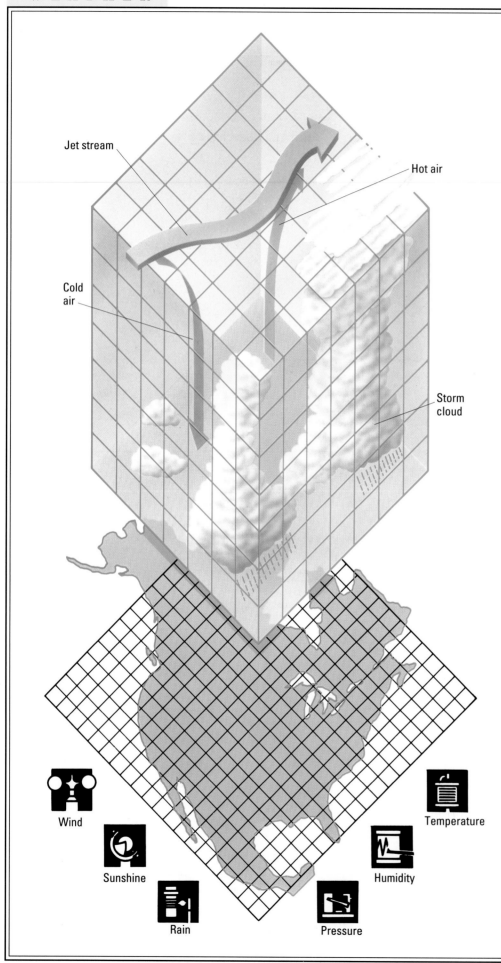

Jet stream

Hot air

Cold air

Storm cloud

Wind

Sunshine

Rain

Pressure

Humidity

Temperature

WEATHER FORECAST

To forecast the weather over a region such as a continent, meteorologists (scientists who study weather) divide the region into a number of three-dimensional cells. Instruments at weather stations in each cell record conditions such as air pressure, humidity, and temperature. These readings are fed into a computer, which uses a mathematical model to predict how the weather will change from cell to cell.

warm air south of the polar front with the cooler air north of the polar front. Frontal cyclones are most likely to strike the United States during the fall and winter (see CYCLONE; FRONT; JET STREAM; STORM).

A cyclone called a tropical cyclone is a severe storm that develops over warm waters near the equator. It usually develops during the late summer and early fall. A very strong tropical cyclone that develops in the West Indies or the eastern Pacific Ocean is called a hurricane. Hurricanes sometimes strike the United States as far north as New England. They may cause widespread damage. A very strong tropical cyclone that develops over the western Pacific Ocean is called a typhoon (see HURRICANE).

Elements of the weather Many different components make up the weather. Some conditions of the atmosphere can be measured. These include temperature, air pressure, wind, and moisture.

The temperature is how warm or cold the air is. The temperature varies according to location. In

WEATHER STATION
This remote weather station has instruments powered by a solar panel. The instruments measure such conditions as wind speed and direction, humidity, temperature, and rainfall. The readings are sent via a cable to a national weather-monitoring system.

CLOUD COVER
The amount of clouds affects the weather on a daily basis, particularly the air temperature. Also the type of clouds can give an indication of the weather to come.

atmosphere. These winds are called the jet stream. The jet stream loops around the earth, causing high-pressure (good weather) systems and low-pressure (storm) systems to form. Low-pressure systems that form along the polar front in the Northern Hemisphere are called frontal cyclones. A frontal cyclone gets much of its energy from the mixing of the polar regions and high mountain ranges, the temperature is usually cold. In the tropics, the temperature is always hot at low altitudes. In the middle latitudes, the temperature changes between hot and cold. These differences are influenced by the angle of the sun's rays, cloud cover (the amount of clouds), the season, and the time of day. The temperature is measured by an instrument called a thermometer (see CLOUD; TEMPERATURE; THERMOMETER; TROPICS).

Air pressure is important to weather forecasters. An air mass of high pressure usually means good weather. A low-pressure air mass usually means bad weather. In the Northern Hemisphere, high-pressure systems have a clockwise flow of air around the area of highest pressure. Low-pressure systems have a counterclockwise flow of air around the area of lowest pressure. Meteorologists measure the air pressure with an instrument called a barometer. If the barometer reading is dropping, weather forecasters predict poor weather. A rise in the pressure signals better weather (see BAROMETER).

The wind is the flow of air. In temperate regions (middle latitudes), wind is often caused by air flowing from a high-pressure system into a low-pressure system. Meteorologists can predict weather changes by tracking the wind flow. The speed and direction of the wind are measured by an instrument called an anemometer (see ANEMOMETER).

Moisture in the atmosphere forms clouds. The clouds produce different kinds of precipitation, including hail, rain, sleet, and snow. The amount of water vapor in the air is called the humidity. Radar is often used to gather information about approaching precipitation. Radar can tell the difference between the small raindrops of an ordinary cloud and the large raindrops produced by a storm.

WEATHER SATELLITE
Large-scale weather patterns are tracked by satellites orbiting high above the earth. For example, satellite photographs allow forecasters to plot the course of a hurricane and warn people of possible danger.

Radar can also tell the meteorologists in which direction the precipitation is headed. Actual rainfall is measured with instruments called rain gauges (see HUMIDITY; RADAR; RAIN GAUGE).

Meteorologists make other readings, including visibility (the distance a person can see), cloud cover, cloud heights, and jet stream measurements. Many of the readings, such as cloud cover, are done by observation. Others, such as jet stream measurements, are done by radiosondes. Meteorological satellites, commonly called metsats, photograph the atmosphere from space (see RADIOSONDE; SATELLITE).

Weather forecasting Atmospheric conditions are measured throughout the day by weather stations around the country. The information is sent from station to station, often by computers. Meteorologists then use the information to make weather forecasts. Weather maps are a major part of weather forecasts. Meteorologists may draw lines of equal barometric pressure, called isobars, and lines of equal temperature, called isotherms, to show the present weather patterns (see ISOBAR AND ISOTHERM). Maps are also prepared to show the condition of the upper atmosphere. This is important for tracking the jet stream.

Weather forecasts are most accurate for twenty-four to forty-eight hours. Long-range forecasts are usually computer predictions about the weather over the next week or month. Long-range forecasts are not nearly as accurate as short-range forecasts. 🔬 PROJECT 22, 23, 24, 25, 39

SHORT-RANGE FORECASTS

Weather satellites allow meteorologists to make accurate short-range forecasts. These weather maps show how the weather over the North Atlantic changed at intervals of twelve hours.

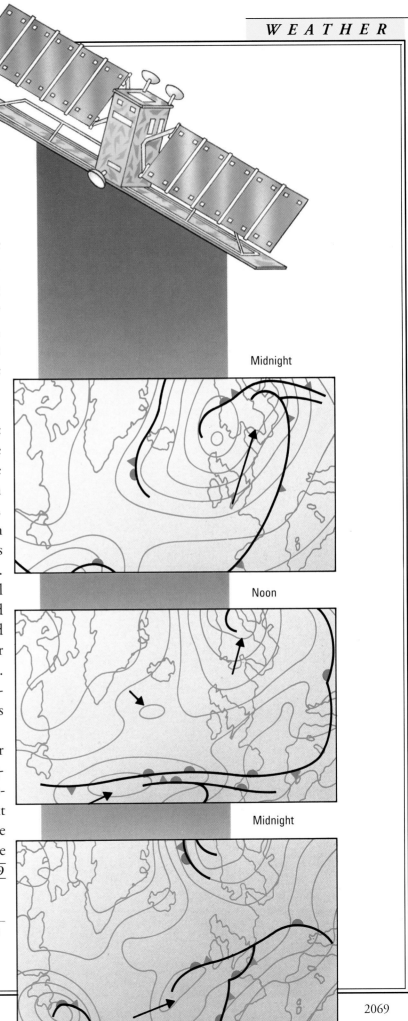

Midnight

Noon

Midnight

WEATHERING Weathering is the breaking and wearing down of rocks by the weather. Weathering plays an important part in the formation of soil and in the natural erosion (wearing down) of the land. There are two main kinds of weathering: mechanical weathering and chemical weathering (see EROSION; ROCK; SOIL).

Rocks are broken apart by mechanical weathering in several ways. Sometimes, rainwater enters a crack in a rock. If the temperature drops below 32°F [0°C], the water freezes into ice. When water freezes, it expands. This expansion may break the rock. Weathered rocks occurring on a slope or the side of a mountain may tumble down to form sloping piles of rubble (broken stones) called scree.

The surfaces of desert rocks are very hot during the day but cool off quickly at night. Extremes of temperatures cause the surface layer to expand and contract (move in and out). This may cause the rock's surface layer to break or peel off in a process called exfoliation.

Plant roots break some rocks apart. The plant roots grow into narrow cracks. As the plant grows, the roots become thicker and break the rocks.

The main agent of chemical weathering is water. Water can dissolve many minerals found in rocks. After the removal of these minerals, the rocks may crumble.

Rainwater may contain carbon dioxide dissolved from the atmosphere. This forms a very weak acid (carbonic acid). When such rainwater comes in contact with limestone, it dissolves the limestone. Karst topography is formed in this way.
See also LIMESTONE.

WEBER (wĕb'ər) The weber is a unit in the metric system that measures the strength of magnetic flux. The magnetic flux is the magnetic field strength multiplied by the area through which the field passes (see MAGNETIC FIELD). The weber is equal to the amount of flux that, linking an electric circuit of one turn (one loop of wire), produces in it an electromotive force of one volt as the flux is reduced to zero at a uniform rate in one second. The weber is named after the German physicist Wilhelm Weber (1804–1891).
See also CIRCUIT, ELECTRIC; ELECTROMOTIVE FORCE; FLUX; MAGNETISM; METRIC SYSTEM; VOLT.

WEBWORM *Webworm* is the name for various types of moth caterpillars that spin a silky web around part or all of their foodplant. Webworms live in groups. They usually feed only on the part of the plant under their web, and make the web larger as they move on to new parts. One type of webworm found in the eastern United States is the

WEATHERING

Throughout time, weathering can wear away even the hardest rock. Weathering plays an important part in the formation of new soil and in the natural erosion of the land. This weathered sandstone structure in Capitol Reef National Park, Utah, is aptly called "The Castle."

WEBWORM

Webworms are caterpillars that spin a silky web around part or all of their food. One type of webworm found in the eastern United States is the fall webworm (right). The web of the fall webworm becomes large enough at times to enclose a human being.

fall webworm. This webworm eats the leaves of fruit and forest trees. At times, the web of the fall webworm is large enough to enclose a human being. The caterpillars grow into small white moths.

See also BUTTERFLY AND MOTH; CATERPILLAR.

WEED A weed is any plant that grows where it is not wanted. Most weeds are plants that readily invade open ground and grow quickly. They reduce the quality and quantity of desired or useful plants by competing with them for space, water, nutrients, and sunlight.

Weeds cause the destruction of billions of dollars' worth of crops around the world every year. Crops include food plants, such as corn, and ornamental plants, such as flowers and lawn grasses (see CROP).

WEED—Competition
Poppies (left) and docks (below) invade fields of cereal crops, competing with them for space, water, nutrients, and sunlight.

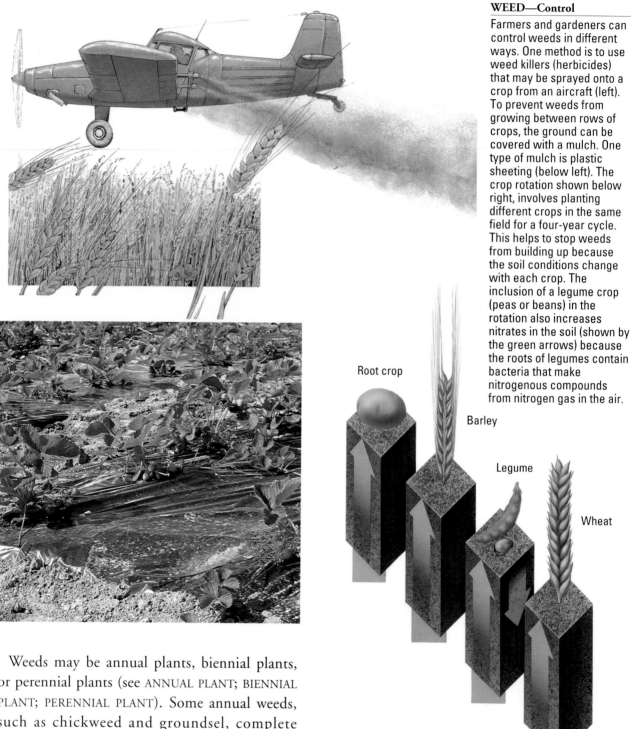

Farmers and gardeners can control weeds in different ways. One method is to use weed killers (herbicides) that may be sprayed onto a crop from an aircraft (left). To prevent weeds from growing between rows of crops, the ground can be covered with a mulch. One type of mulch is plastic sheeting (below left). The crop rotation shown below right, involves planting different crops in the same field for a four-year cycle. This helps to stop weeds from building up because the soil conditions change with each crop. The inclusion of a legume crop (peas or beans) in the rotation also increases nitrates in the soil (shown by the green arrows) because the roots of legumes contain bacteria that make nitrogenous compounds from nitrogen gas in the air.

Root crop

Barley

Legume

Wheat

Weeds may be annual plants, biennial plants, or perennial plants (see ANNUAL PLANT; BIENNIAL PLANT; PERENNIAL PLANT). Some annual weeds, such as chickweed and groundsel, complete their entire life cycle in only a few weeks. In a single growing season, these weeds may produce several generations of weeds. This means that even though the first generation of weeds may be controlled, there are soon more generations that have to be controlled. Some weeds, such as docks and thistles, are especially difficult to get rid of because they have extensive root systems (see ROOT).

There are four methods that farmers, gardeners, and homeowners can use to reduce weeds. The first method has to do with the way crops are planted. For example, seed mixtures that are free of weed seeds can be planted. Farmers also can rotate their crops. Crop rotation involves the planting of different crops in the same field each year. This may help to prevent weeds from building up on a certain area, because the soil conditions change with each crop. In smaller areas, such as flower gardens, mulching can be used. Mulching involves covering the ground around crops with wood chips, grass cuttings, or plastic. The mulch keeps weeds from growing because they do not receive enough light and air.

A second method of controlling weeds uses machines or other tools. For example, large machines called cultivators can be used by farmers to dig up weeds. Mowing machines can be used to cut down tall weeds. In small areas, homeowners or gardeners can use a tool called a hoe to dig up weeds.

A third method of controlling weeds uses the natural biological enemies of weeds (see BIOLOGICAL CONTROL). These enemies may be certain insects, other small animals, or even bacteria that attack specific weeds.

The final method of controlling weeds involves the use of chemicals called herbicides. However, herbicides may be poisonous to humans and other animals.

See also AGRICULTURE; HERBICIDE.

WEEVIL *Weevil* is the name for a group of beetles in which the head is drawn out into a snout. Most weevils belong to the family Curculionidae, which, with about 60,000 members, is the largest family in the animal kingdom (see ANIMAL KINGDOM). There are jaws at the end of the weevil's snout. Antennae are located halfway up the snout (see ANTENNAE). Weevils are found on plants throughout the world. Many species are brightly colored. The colors are sometimes provided by a coating of scales or powder. This coating rubs off easily.

Many weevils lack hind wings and so are unable to fly. Their front wings, or elytra, may not be movable. The larvae, also called grubs, have no legs. Larvae often feed inside plant tissues. Flower, leaves, roots, seeds, and stems are all attacked. The female weevil often uses her snout to drill a hole for her eggs (see LARVA).

Many species of weevils are serious pests. For example, the boll weevil causes great losses in cotton fields (see BOLL WEEVIL). Grain weevils, which first fed on the seeds of wild grasses, have become troublesome pests where grain is stored. Pine weevils feed on the bark of young conifer shoots and cause distortion of the branches (see CONIFER). Weevil larvae, rather than adults, usually do most of the damage.

See also BEETLE.

WEEVIL

The head of a weevil is drawn out into a snout. The family to which weevils belong is the largest in the animal kingdom.

WEIGHT (wāt) Weight is the force put forth by gravity on an object (see GRAVITY). It is very easy to confuse weight with mass. However, they are not the same thing. The mass of an object is the amount of material that it contains. The weight is the force with which that amount of material is pulled to the ground by gravity (see MASS). Scientists using the metric system measure mass in kilograms and measure weight in the unit of force called the newton (see METRIC SYSTEM; NEWTON). Many people, however, use measurements such as kilograms, pounds, and tons for both weight and mass.

The pull of gravity varies slightly in different parts of the world. Thus, an object may weigh less at the top of Mount Everest in the Himalaya mountains than at sea level. If the object were taken to the moon, its weight would be only one-sixth of its weight on Earth. This is because the moon's gravity is one-sixth of the earth's. The mass of the object would not change, however. **PROJECT 2**

WEIGHTLESSNESS

Weightlessness (wāt′lĭs nĕs) is the condition in which objects appear to have no weight. Weight is caused by the force of gravity pulling objects toward the center of the earth. There appears to be no gravitational force acting on a weightless object. The condition is also known as zero gravity (see GRAVITY; WEIGHT).

Weightlessness can occur when an object is so far from the earth that the earth's gravity is too small to have an effect. Weightlessness also occurs when a spacecraft is orbiting the earth. In orbit, the spacecraft is continually falling towards the earth because of the earth's gravity, but it is also moving forward at great speed. The combination of the two motions makes the spacecraft move in a circular path around the earth. The spacecraft remains at the same height above the earth's surface. It is said to be weightless.

Weightlessness causes problems in orbiting spacecraft. Anything that is not fixed or tied down floats around. Astronauts use special devices to be able to eat and drink. Crew members have to learn to adjust the vigor of their actions to keep from crashing into the walls and equipment. Sometimes, weightlessness causes nausea and giddiness, because the part of the ear responsible for balance is upset. Astronauts are able to adapt to weightlessness in a short time through training (see ASTRONAUTICS).

On Earth, body muscles always get a certain amount of exercise because they are being used to work against gravity. To overcome the effect of weightlessness in a spacecraft, regular exercise is essential to keep the muscles in good condition. Also, while in orbit, astronauts tend to "grow" taller. This is because the pads of cartilage between the bones of the spine are no longer under pressure from gravity, and they expand. The increase in height, which may be as much as 2 in. [5 cm], disappears when the astronauts return to Earth.

Under weightless conditions, it is possible to conduct certain scientific experiments that are impossible on Earth. For example, absolutely perfect crystals can be grown. Also, alloys (combinations) of different metals can be formed that are very difficult to make under the pull of gravity.

SPACE WALK
Astronauts on space shuttles are trained to work in weightless conditions.

WELDING AND CUTTING Welding is a means of joining similar metals by melting them, bringing them together so that they fuse (blend together), and then allowing the fused metal parts to harden (see METAL AND METALLURGY).

Welding involves very high temperatures. The temperatures are often produced by jets of burning gases. Oxygen and acetylene are often used, producing an oxyacetylene flame. Another flame that can be used is the oxyhydrogen (oxygen and hydrogen) flame (see OXYACETYLENE TORCH).

The flame heats the metal parts to be joined until the surfaces become molten (melted) metal and fuse together. Additional metal may be added to the joint by melting wires or rods. The extra metal is added and built up around the parts to make a solid joint.

WELDING AND CUTTING

Welders use hot flames in their work. A welder in a shipyard (above) is using a high-temperature torch to join two pieces of steel.

There are many different kinds of welding. Electric arc welding uses a heavy current of electricity passed between electrodes (see ARC, ELECTRIC; ELECTRICITY; ELECTRODE). In atomic hydrogen welding, a stream of hydrogen gas is passed between two electrodes made of the metal tungsten, and an electric arc is struck between the electrodes. Atomic hydrogen welding is used for high-quality alloy steels. An alloy is a combination of two or more metals. Other kinds of welding use beams of electrons, beams of laser light, and streams of gas so hot that they become plasmas (see ELECTRON; LASER; PLASMA (PHYSICS)).

Welding is an extremely important process in engineering. It may be used to join metal pipes, to fix parts of bridges tightly together, and to construct the metal frames of buildings. It is also used in shipbuilding and in the aircraft industry (see AIRPLANE; ENGINEERING; SHIPS AND SHIPBUILDING). Using rivets or nuts and bolts to join parts in a structure adds weight to the structure. The advantage of welding over such ways of joining parts is that it does not add as much weight.

Cutting through metals by means of concentrated, very hot flames or laser beams is widely used in industry. Thermal cutting is a type of cutting that is often used in engineering and shipbuilding. A cutting torch is used. The torch heats the steel to the point just before the steel is about to melt. A jet of oxygen is then passed through the center of the flame, and the iron in the steel turns into iron oxide. The burnt metal sprays from the other side of the cut in showers of sparks.

This method can only be used on steel that does not contain much chromium (see CHROMIUM; STEEL). Steel that contains a high proportion of chromium forms oxides that burn at a much higher temperature. To counteract this, powdered iron may be blown in with the jet of oxygen. This lowers the melting point of the waste metal, or slag.

See also MELTING POINT; SOLDERING AND BRAZING.

WELL A well is a human-made hole in the ground. Fluids (gases or liquids), such as water, natural gas, and petroleum (oil), are withdrawn from

WELL—Oil
Most oil wells are deep drilled wells. If the cap at the top of the well is damaged, it has to be replaced. This worker is cutting bolts on a damaged well head.

WELL—Water
People who live in areas where there are no public water systems get their water from wells (below).

wells are made using an auger, which is a screwlike device. Bored wells may be up to 100 ft. [30 m] deep. Drilled wells are made with special drilling equipment, such as a long pipe with a diamond tip. Drilled wells may be more than 10,000 ft. [3,047 m] deep (see DRILLING).

The fluids in wells often have to be pumped to the surface (see PUMP). A kind of well called an artesian well does not rely on pumps to withdraw the fluid. Instead, natural underground pressures bring the fluid to the surface.　PROJECT 17

WERTHEIMER, MAX (1880–1943) Max Wertheimer was a German psychologist. He is best known for founding a school of psychological thought based on the concept of gestalt (see PSYCHOLOGY). *Gestalt* is a German word that means "pattern" or "form."

The idea of gestalt psychology is that every experience is a complete happening. The opposite of gestalt is the idea that experiences are composed of many small parts. In gestalt theory, the many small parts add up to more than just their sum. For example, a picture of a cat is not just a collection of lines, but an image of a cat. This image may produce different feelings in different people. According to Wertheimer, because we see things as whole pictures, that is how our minds work.

See also PERCEPTION.

wells. Solid substances, such as sulfur, may also be removed from the ground using wells. A spring is a kind of natural water well (see SPRING AND GEYSER).

There are several different kinds of wells. For example, some shallow wells, called dug wells, are dug by hand, using simple tools. Driven wells are made using a pipe with a point on the end. Driven wells may be up to about 50 ft. [15 m] deep. Bored

Whales are aquatic mammals belonging to the order Cetacea (see MAMMAL). A few species live in fresh water, but most species live in the salt water of the oceans. A whale has a streamlined shape and a powerful tail to drive it forward. The tail has two large horizontal fins or flukes that produce the driving force by beating strongly up and down. Flippers at the front of the animal's body are used for steering and balance. The hind limbs of whales have completely disappeared, apart from a few small bones inside the body. Body hair has also disappeared, giving whales a smoother outline and less resistance to water. Instead of hair, whales are insulated by a thick layer of fat, called blubber, under the skin. The blubber may be as much as 2 ft. [61 cm] thick on some parts of the body. Besides protecting the animal against the cold, the blubber is an important food reserve.

Most of the best-known whales are large creatures. For example, the blue whale reaches a length of more than 100 ft. [30 m]. However, many whales, such as dolphins and porpoises, are small. Some are only 5 to 6 ft. [1.5 to 1.8 m] long (see BLUE WHALE; DOLPHIN; PORPOISE).

LEAPING HUMPBACK

Despite its enormous size, a humpback whale (right) can leap clear of the water by pushing with its powerful tail.

RIGHT WHALE

The right whale (below) has pale patches on its belly. Its huge head takes up more than one third of the length of its body.

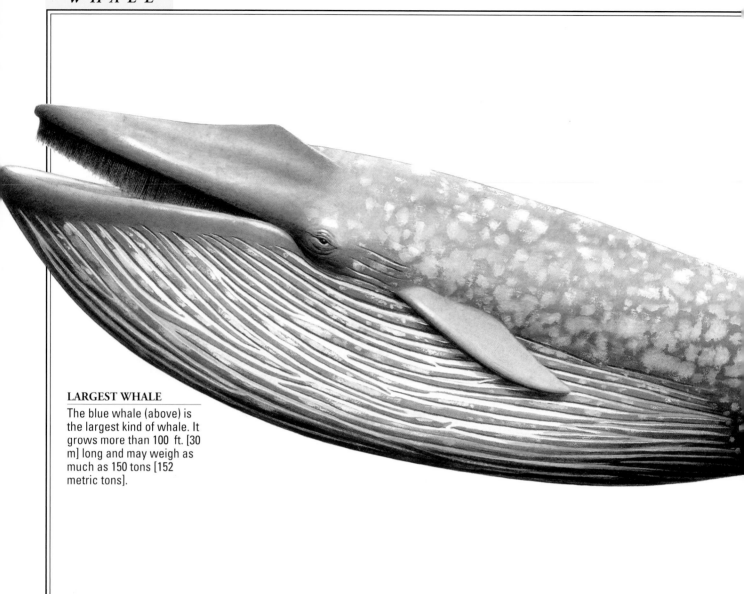

LARGEST WHALE

The blue whale (above) is the largest kind of whale. It grows more than 100 ft. [30 m] long and may weigh as much as 150 tons [152 metric tons].

MOTHER AND BABY

The skin of this mother gray whale (right) is covered with large clusters of barnacles. The young calf is sleek and smooth-skinned.

Whales live entirely in water. Sometimes, whales are stranded on the shore. Although they are air-breathing animals, they soon die because their great weight keeps them from expanding (opening out) the chest cavity. They can breathe easily when afloat, because the water supports most of their weight.

The bottle-nosed whale has been known to stay under water for about two hours. The sperm whale can dive down to depths of five hundred fathoms, which is over half a mile [0.8 km] down (see FATHOM; SPERM WHALE). However, such long and deep dives are unusual. Most whale dives last between ten and thirty minutes. Whales have special mechanisms that help them stay under water. When they inhale, they renew about nine-tenths of the air in their lungs. When human beings inhale, only about one-fourth of the air is renewed. Whales, therefore, have a fairly large supply of fresh air to start with. They also have an additional oxygen supply in the muscles, where oxygen is loosely held in combination with a pigment called myoglobin (see PIGMENT).

Another thing that helps whales hold their breath for long periods of time is their low sensitivity to carbon dioxide in their blood. It is the carbon dioxide building up in a human being's blood that affects the brain and makes the human being take another breath (see BREATHING).

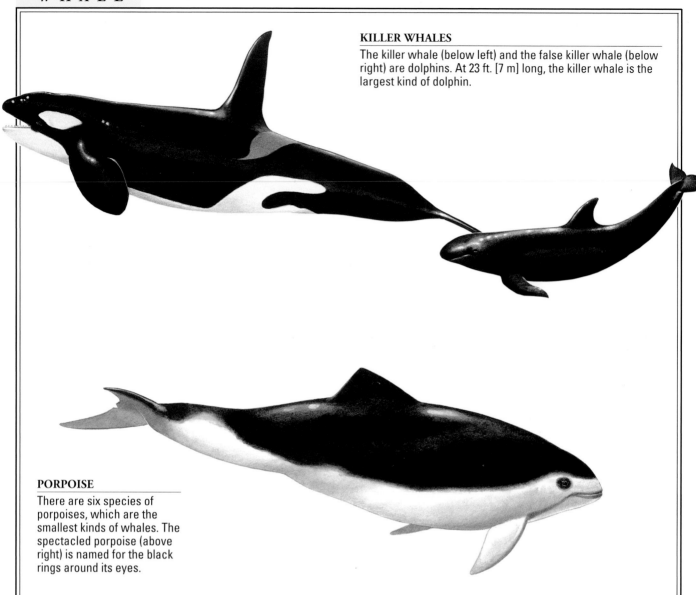

KILLER WHALES
The killer whale (below left) and the false killer whale (below right) are dolphins. At 23 ft. [7 m] long, the killer whale is the largest kind of dolphin.

PORPOISE
There are six species of porpoises, which are the smallest kinds of whales. The spectacled porpoise (above right) is named for the black rings around its eyes.

When a whale surfaces to renew its air supply, it needs only to push the top of its snout out of the water. This is because the nostril, or blowhole, is at the top of the head. The expelled air is forced out strongly to form the spout, or blow.

Whales are divided into two groups—toothed whales and baleen whales. Toothed whales have teeth. Baleen whales do not have teeth. Instead, they have hundreds of thin plates in their mouths called baleen. Baleen whales use these plates to strain small organisms from the water. The mouth is first filled with water; then the water is forced out through the baleen by the tongue. The organisms caught in the baleen are swept into the stomach by the tongue. All baleen whales are large animals and are usually found in cold waters. They include the blue and the right whales (see RIGHT WHALE).

Toothed whales, which include most species, generally have many conical teeth and eat mainly squids and fishes. One African river dolphin feeds mostly on plants. Other toothed whales include the narwhal and the sperm whale (see NARWHAL).

The future of many of the larger kinds of whales is uncertain. Whalers have killed so many blue, bowhead, humpback, and right whales that those species are threatened with extinction (see ENDANGERED SPECIES; EXTINCTION). Overhunting has also greatly reduced the number of fin and sei whales. Also, whales may soon be competing with humans for food. Some nations are researching the possibility of krill as a source of protein for humans. Krill is the chief food of baleen whales in Antarctic waters.

See also KRILL.

Wheat is one of the world's most important food crops. Only rice feeds more people than wheat (see RICE). However, wheat crops cover more of the earth's surface than rice or any other crop. Farmers of the world grow over 18 billion bushels of wheat a year. Hundreds of millions of people throughout the world use wheat as their main source of food.

The wheat plant belongs to the grass family, Gramineae or Poaceae (see GRASS). It is bright green in color until harvest time, when it turns golden brown. Wheat plants grow about 4.3 ft. [1.3 m] high. The leaves are long and slender. The wheat head, which holds the kernels or grains, is at the top of the main stem. The average plant produces fifty kernels of wheat. The kernels are about 0.12 to 0.25 in. [3 to 6 mm] long. A kernel can be divided into four parts—germ, bran, endosperm, and chaff. The germ is the embryonic plant, which starts to grow after the seed is planted. Wheat germ is used in some breakfast cereals and is also eaten as a food alone. The bran is made up of several layers. It protects the germ and endosperm much like a shell protects a nut. The bran is used primarily in livestock feed. The endosperm is the most important part of the wheat kernel. It makes up about 85 percent of the kernel and provides the food for the growing embryo. The endosperm is used in making flour for bread and other baked goods. It contains starch and gluten, a substance that makes dough rise in the presence of yeast. The chaff consists of the stalks and husks, or outer coverings, of the kernels.

Wheat is generally harvested by giant machines called combines. Combines cut, thresh (separate the germ from the chaff and stalks), and clean the wheat. The kernels are then stored in tall cylindrical buildings called grain elevators. Later, the kernels may be transported to factories, where they are milled (ground) into flour for use in baking. About 700 million bushels of wheat are ground into 32 billion lb. [15 billion kg] of flour each year in the United States. The average person in the United States uses about 117 lb. [53 kg] of wheat a year.

Wheat is also made into breakfast cereals and livestock feeds. China is the largest producer of wheat in the world, with a yearly crop of over 3 billion bushels. The former Soviet Union ranks second, and the United States ranks third. The top wheat-producing states include Kansas, North Dakota, and Texas.

HARVESTING

Wheat is the second most important cereal crop after rice and is the main source of food for hundreds of millions of people. The unripe ears of wheat (above) bear tiny yellow flowers. When ripe, the crop is harvested using a combine harvester (left).

WHEEL
The Ferris wheel (right) is a popular ride at an amusement park. It is also one of the largest wheels made. The development of the wheel from log rollers to spoked wheels is shown below.

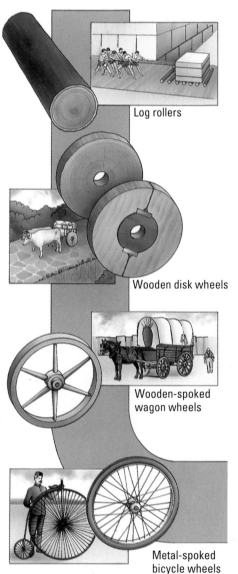

Log rollers

Wooden disk wheels

Wooden-spoked wagon wheels

Metal-spoked bicycle wheels

WHEEL A wheel is a circular frame of wood, metal, or other hard material that can be attached at its center to an axle, thus allowing it to rotate. It can be made as a solid disk, or in the form of a ring or rim that is strengthened by spokes, which are thin sticklike pieces of wood or metal that spread out from a central hub.

Although the invention of the wheel is considered to be one of the great milestones in the history of the human race, it is not known exactly when and where it happened (see INVENTION). Many archaeologists believe that the wheel was invented in ancient Mesopotamia sometime during the fourth century B.C. and then spread to the rest of the world. The first wheels were solid disks. By early in the second century B.C., the spoked wheel was invented, probably in northern Syria or in Anatolia (present-day Turkey). **PROJECT 50**

WHIPPOORWILL The whippoorwill is a bird found in North America. The bird is named for its whistled call, which sounds like "whip-poor-will, whip-poor-will."

The whippoorwill's body is about 10 in. [25 cm] long. The bird has brown, spotted feathers that blend in with wooded surroundings. Whippoorwills are normally active at night. Because of their soft feathers, whippoorwills fly silently. Like swallows, they fly with their bills open to catch insects (see SWALLOW).

The female usually lays two eggs on the ground. The eggs are white and are marked with lilac and brown. Whippoorwills, like many birds, are a natural help to farmers. The birds eat some insects that often damage crops.
See also BIRD.

WHIRLIGIG (hwûr′lĭ gĭg′) The whirligigs are a group of seven hundred species of water beetles that belong to the family Gyrinidae. They swim in circles on the surface of quiet ponds and lakes. Their smooth, oval bodies are a shiny bluish black or olive green. The front legs are long and adapted for grabbing and holding small insects that fall onto the surface of the water. The middle and rear legs are broad, paddle shaped, and fringed with hairs. The whirligig uses these broad legs to move itself forward across the water's surface. If threatened, a whirligig may release a foul-smelling, milky liquid.

The compound eyes of the whirligig are divided into upper and lower halves (see EYE AND VISION). The upper halves watch the activity above the water's surface, while the lower halves watch the activity below the water's surface. When alarmed, they dive down to hide in the mud or among the plants. Whirligigs have well-developed wings and are excellent fliers.

A female whirligig deposits her eggs on underwater plants. The eggs hatch into larvae that breathe through gills and prey on aquatic insects.
See also BEETLE; GILLS; LARVA.

WHIRLIGIG
A crowd of whirligigs scurry across the surface of a pond.

WHITE DWARF A white dwarf is a star that has almost run out of nuclear fuel and is nearing the end of its life (see DWARF STAR; STAR). It is made up of the parts of atoms—electrons and nuclei—squeezed together very tightly by gravity. This material is very dense, about 100,000 times as dense as water. A white dwarf star has a mass close to that of the sun, but a diameter only about as large as that of the earth or smaller.

An estimated 10 billion of the 100 billion stars in the Milky Way galaxy have died and produced white dwarfs (see GALAXY; MILKY WAY). The best-known white dwarf is the star called Sirius B, which orbits around Sirius, the brightest star in the night sky. After billions of years, a white dwarf cools down and stops shining. It becomes a dark object called a black dwarf.

A white dwarf cannot have a mass larger than 1.4 times that of the sun. When a star of greater mass runs out of nuclear fuel, it collapses to become either a neutron star or a black hole (see BLACK HOLE; NEUTRON STAR).

WHITEFISH A whitefish is a freshwater fish that belongs to the family Salmonidae. It is closely related to the salmon and trout (see SALMON; TROUT). It is a silvery fish that lives in cold northern lakes and rivers. Whitefish feed on plankton and are eaten by many other fish and animals, including humans (see PLANKTON). The whitefish was an important commercial fish in the Great Lakes until overfishing and environmental changes caused the decline of the fish. However, the government has worked to protect the fish and build up its numbers. There are about twenty species of whitefish in North America.
See also FISH.

WHITNEY, ELI (1765–1825) Eli Whitney was an American inventor. He was born in Westborough, Massachusetts. He was studying law in Georgia when he visited a cotton plantation (large farm). During his visit, he saw there was a need for a machine to separate the seeds from the cotton fibers. He built his first cotton gin (a shortened version of the word *engine*) in 1793, which could pick out the seeds from the cotton as fast as fifty people could. The cotton gin helped the cotton industry grow (see COTTON).

When Whitney made a contract with the American government in 1798 to make muskets (guns), he developed an even greater invention. Until then, guns were all made by hand. Each gun was made of parts that fit only that gun. Whitney designed machine tools that allowed even unskilled workers to make perfect parts. Guns could be assembled from these parts without any more machine work being done on them. Also, guns with broken parts could be repaired with spare parts. This was the beginning of mass production.
See also MASS PRODUCTION.

WHITTLE, SIR FRANK (1907–)

Frank Whittle is the British engineer who invented the jet engine. He was born in Coventry, England. He became a fighter pilot in the Royal Air Force (RAF). Later, he was sent by the RAF to study engineering at Cambridge University. As an engineer, he worked on the development of gas turbines for the jet propulsion of aircraft (see GAS TURBINE; JET PROPULSION). In May 1941, Whittle's first jet-powered aircraft was tested. By the end of World War II (1939–1945), many jet airplanes were being flown. Since then, jet engines have been developed so that all large commercial and military planes are powered by them. All these engines are based on Whittle's design. Whittle is a faculty member at the U.S. Naval Academy in Annapolis, Maryland. His many honors and awards include the Charles Stark Draper Prize, presented by the National Academy of Engineering in 1991.
See also AIRPLANE.

WIENER, NORBERT (1894–1964)

Norbert Wiener was an American mathematician and the founder of the science of cybernetics. He was born in Columbia, Missouri. Wiener was a highly talented child. He could read and write when he was only three years old. He received a doctoral degree from Harvard University in Massachusetts when he was eighteen.

Wiener joined the Massachusetts Institute of Technology in 1919. He retired as a professor in 1960. While there, he pioneered the science of cybernetics. Cybernetics is the study of control and communication in animals and machines. Wiener was especially interested in the similarity between computers and the human brain. He wrote books on the subject of cybernetics and contributed greatly to the theory and technology of automation. Wiener was awarded the National Medal of Science by U.S. President Lyndon B. Johnson a few weeks before his death.
See also AUTOMATION; COMPUTER; CYBERNETICS.

WILLIAMS, DANIEL HALE (1858–1931)

Daniel Hale Williams is famous for being the first surgeon to repair a tear in the pericardium, or sac surrounding the heart. He performed the surgery in 1893 (see SURGERY).

Williams, an African-American, was born in Hollidaysburg, Pennsylvania. In 1883, he received his doctoral degree in medicine from Chicago Medical College in Illinois. In 1891, he founded Chicago's Provident Hospital. This was the first hospital in the United States to accept patients of all races. The hospital also helped train African-Americans to become doctors and nurses. In 1913, the American College of Surgeons was formed. The American College of Surgeons is a professional organization that is concerned with the education of surgeons. Williams was the only African-American among the group's first members.

WILLOW FAMILY

The willow family (Salicaceae) contains two genera (plural of *genus*): *Populus,* the poplars, with thirty-five species of deciduous trees; and *Salix,* the willows, with about four hundred species. Willows are deciduous trees and shrubs with simple leaves (see DECIDUOUS TREE). Some of them creep over the ground and are no more than 1 to 2 in. [2.5 to 5 cm] high (see LEAF; SHRUB; TREE). Clusters of male or female flowers form catkins on separate plants (see CATKIN). In the genus *Populus,* the catkins droop from the branches and are pollinated by the wind. In the genus *Salix,*

WILLOW FAMILY
The willow family includes many species of the genus *Salix*, such as the ornamental weeping willow (left). It also includes species of the genus *Populus*, the poplars, which bear hanging catkins (above).

the catkins are upright and are usually pollinated by insects. Most members of the willow family grow in northern temperate areas (see CLIMATE).

The black willow is a valuable lumber tree that grows in the eastern United States (see LUMBER). Weeping willow and pussy willow are two familiar members of the willow family.

See also POPLAR.

WILTING Wilting is the drooping and drying out of the leaves and stem of a plant. Wilting may be caused by lack of water. Quite often, however, wilting is the symptom of a plant disease. These diseases may be caused by bacteria, fungi, or viruses (see BACTERIA; FUNGUS; VIRUS).

A plant whose wilting is caused by lack of water may recover through watering. However, most disease-caused wilting is fatal to the plant. Preventive measures against wilting should be taken while the plant is still young.

See also PLANT DISEASE.

WILTING
These pictures show a snapdragon plant before (left) and after (right) it wilted. Wilting may be caused by either lack of water or a plant disease.

WIND

Wind is the movement of air across the earth's surface. Wind has an important effect on the weather. For example, when cold air meets warm air, clouds and precipitation often form (see AIR; ATMOSPHERE; CLOUD; PRECIPITATION; WEATHER).

The direction of the wind is the direction from which it comes. For example, a north wind blows from north to south, while a southeast wind blows from southeast to northwest.

The main factor that causes wind is the heating of the atmosphere by the sun. Air that is warmed by the sun rises. This creates a kind of vacuum that is then filled by cooler air (see VACUUM). This process is called circulation. Circulation over the entire earth is called general circulation. Cool air flows away from the North and South poles. Warm air flows from the equator toward the poles (see EQUATOR). The movement of air over the earth's surface is also affected by the rotation (spinning) of the earth. The rotation of the earth forces air blowing toward the equator to curve to the west and air blowing away from the equator to curve to the east. This is called the Coriolis effect (see CORIOLIS EFFECT).

Prevailing winds General circulation produces six large belts of wind that are referred to as the prevailing winds. Two belts of trade winds occur in the area between 30° north latitude and the equator and between 30° south latitude and the equator.

WIND PATTERNS

The prevailing winds around the world form the general pattern shown at left. An area of windless calm at the equator is called the doldrums. Similar calm regions between the trade winds and the westerlies are known as the horse latitudes. The satellite picture (below) shows how spiraling winds have formed two hurricanes.

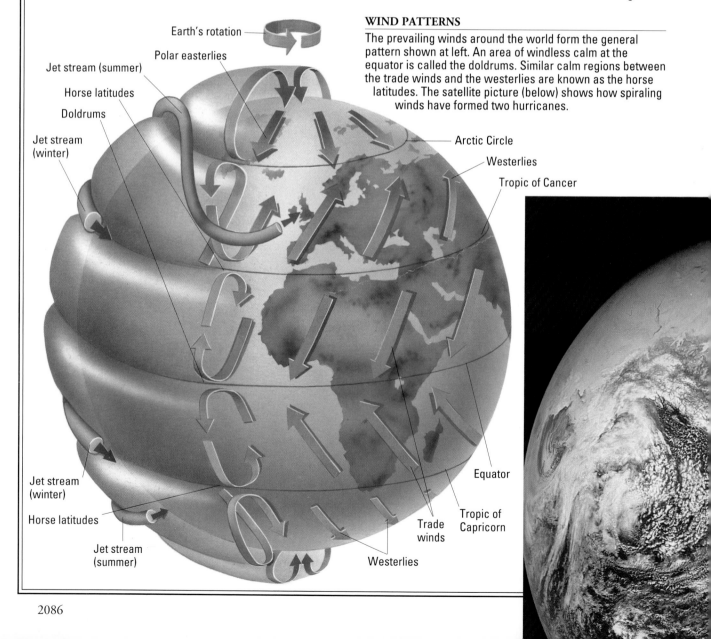

Earth's rotation

Polar easterlies

Jet stream (summer)

Horse latitudes

Doldrums

Jet stream (winter)

Arctic Circle

Westerlies

Tropic of Cancer

Equator

Tropic of Capricorn

Trade winds

Westerlies

Jet stream (winter)

Horse latitudes

Jet stream (summer)

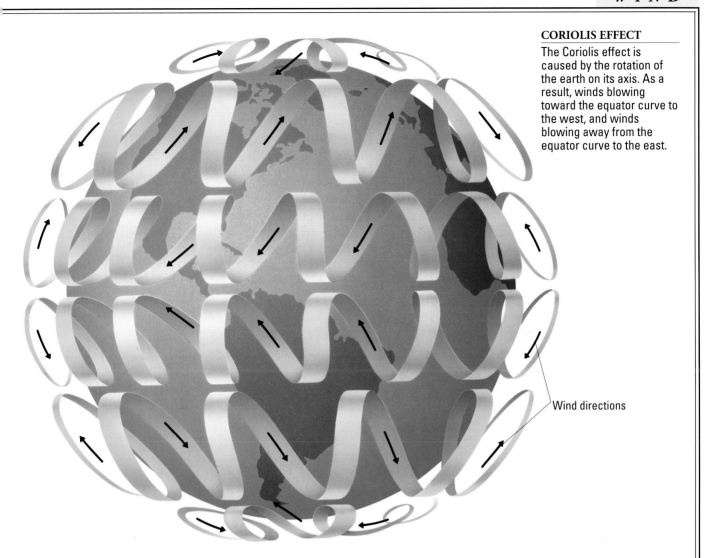

CORIOLIS EFFECT
The Coriolis effect is caused by the rotation of the earth on its axis. As a result, winds blowing toward the equator curve to the west, and winds blowing away from the equator curve to the east.

Wind directions

Trade winds are produced by the action of cool air moving in to replace the warm air near the equator that has risen. Trade winds blow toward the equator, so the Coriolis effect forces them to blow in a general east-to-west direction.

The air that rises at the equator spreads north and south, cools, and descends at about 30° north and south of the equator. Then some of it sweeps back to the equator as the trade winds, while the rest travels toward the poles as the westerlies. Prevailing westerlies blow away from the equator, so the Coriolis effect forces them to blow in a general west-to-east direction. The prevailing westerlies in the Northern Hemisphere play an important role in the weather of the United States.

The last two belts of prevailing winds, called polar easterlies, are winds that occur between the poles and 60° north and south of the equator. The polar easterlies are caused by the movement of

heavy cooler air from the poles toward the equator. The polar easterlies blow toward the equator, and so the Coriolis effect forces them to blow in a general east-to-west direction.

Near the equator, there are no prevailing winds. Instead, there is a calm belt known as the doldrums. In this belt, the intense heat from the sun causes the air to rise and not move across the earth's surface. Some of the air that has risen at the equator moves downward near 30° north and south of the equator. This produces two calm belts called the horse latitudes. This air is dry, so deserts are found at these latitudes (see LATITUDE AND LONGITUDE).

Secondary circulation and local winds

The smaller-scale circulation that causes day-to-day wind changes is called secondary circulation. Secondary circulation covers a relatively small area of the earth. Secondary circulation is usually associated with areas of high and low atmospheric pressure. Air flows into low-pressure areas called cyclones, or lows. Air flows out of high-pressure areas called anticyclones, or highs (see ANTICYCLONE; CYCLONE). When viewed from above in the Northern Hemisphere, air flowing toward a cyclone moves in a counterclockwise direction, and air flowing toward an anticyclone moves in a clockwise direction. In the Southern

Hemisphere, these directions are reversed.

Local winds are winds that occur in very specific areas. A monsoon is a kind of local wind. The best-known monsoons occur in the northern part of the Indian Ocean. Monsoons are caused by the unequal heating of land and the ocean (see MONSOON). During the summer, the land is warmer than the oceans. The land air rises and is replaced by the cooler ocean air. During the winter, the ocean is warmer than the land. The ocean air rises and is replaced by cooler land air. Other local winds include chinooks, foehns, siroccos, and northers. Dry winds that blow down the sides of mountains are called chinooks in the western United States and foehns in Europe. A sirocco is a local wind that carries hot air from the Sahara desert to the

Mediterranean region of Europe. A norther is a cold winter wind that blows over the southern United States and Mexico. It occurs when cold air moves southward from a high-pressure area.

Measurement of wind Wind direction can be determined by devices such as a weather vane or a wind sock. A weather vane spins on a rod to point in the direction from which the wind comes. A wind sock is made of material that blows in the opposite direction from which the wind comes. Wind speed is measured by an instrument called an anemometer (see ANEMOMETER). The speed of very swift winds that occur high in the atmosphere, called jet stream winds, are measured by radiosondes. Radiosondes are balloons equipped with measuring instruments (see JET STREAM; RADIOSONDE). Wind speed can also be measured by observation using a system called the Beaufort scale. The scale is numbered from one to twelve. Each observation has its own number, which corresponds to a speed. For example, wind that causes dust and small branches to move and flags to flap has a Beaufort number of four. It is considered a moderate breeze. A moderate breeze has a speed of 13 to 18 m.p.h. [21 to 29 kph] (see BEAUFORT SCALE). Another kind of measurement, called the wind-chill factor, involves the relationship between wind speed and temperature. The wind-chill factor is an indication of how much colder the wind makes the air feel.

Wind as energy Wind has been used as a source of energy for thousands of years (see ENERGY). Winds have been used to power sailing ships, such as those that brought Europeans to the Americas centuries ago. Winds have long been used to power windmills, which were originally used to grind grain. In the late 1700s, over twenty thousand windmills in the Netherlands turned mechanical devices that pumped water from lowlands along that country's coast. This land could then be used for farming. Today, as fossil fuels grow scarce, wind is receiving increased attention as a source of energy (see FOSSIL FUEL). Wind is renewable and plentiful. Also, wind does not pollute the environment as other sources of energy do, such as the burning of fossil fuels (see POLLUTION).

Wind is being used as a source of energy in several areas. For example, in California, large wind "farms" use wind to turn turbines. The turbines drive a generator, which produces electricity. Many parts of southern California receive their power in this way (see ELECTRICITY; GENERATOR, ELECTRICAL; TURBINE). That amount of wind power saves over 1 billion lb. [453 million kg] of pollutants from entering the atmosphere. The Netherlands continues to use the wind as a source of energy. By the year 2050, the people of the Netherlands expect to meet 20 percent of their energy needs using wind turbines.

See also METEOROLOGY.

 PROJECT 24, 25, 49

WIND POWER
Windmills have been used since ancient times. These windmills with fabric sails are driving irrigation pumps in Thailand.

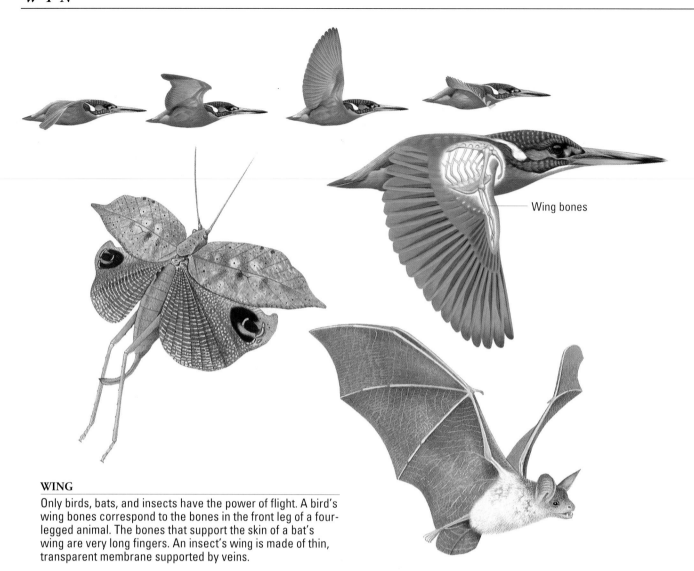

Wing bones

WING

Only birds, bats, and insects have the power of flight. A bird's wing bones correspond to the bones in the front leg of a four-legged animal. The bones that support the skin of a bat's wing are very long fingers. An insect's wing is made of thin, transparent membrane supported by veins.

WING Birds, bats, and insects are the only animals that can fly (see BAT; BIRD; INSECT). They all have wings, but their wings are very different. A bird's wing is a much-modified front leg. It has the same bones as the front leg of any other land-living vertebrate (animal with a backbone), but in different proportions (see VERTEBRATE). Much of the wing is formed by the feathers (see FEATHER). The feathers give the wing the smoothly curved upper surface necessary for producing the lifting force that keeps the bird in the air (see FLIGHT). A bat's wing consists mainly of the arm, but there are no feathers. The wing is made of skin, stretched across the very long fingers and running along the sides of the body to the back legs. Most insects have four wings, but there are no bones in them because insects are invertebrates (animals without a backbone) (see INVERTEBRATE). Each wing is a thin

membrane growing out from the thorax and supported by a network of veins. Some insects fold their wings, but dragonflies and a few other insects cannot. Beetles' forewings are tough and horny and protect the delicate hindwings when folded.
See also SKIN.

PROJECT 38

WIRE Wire is long, thin, flexible metal rod. It has the same cross section, that is, thickness, or diameter, throughout its length. Most wire is made from ductile metals, such as aluminum, brass, copper, gold, silver, steel, or tungsten (see METAL AND METALLURGY). Ductile metals are those that can be drawn out easily. Most wire is made into standard thicknesses, called gauges. The thinnest gauge is 0.000878 in. [0.022301 mm]. The thickest gauge is 0.58 in. [15 mm].

Wire is usually made by pulling metal through a

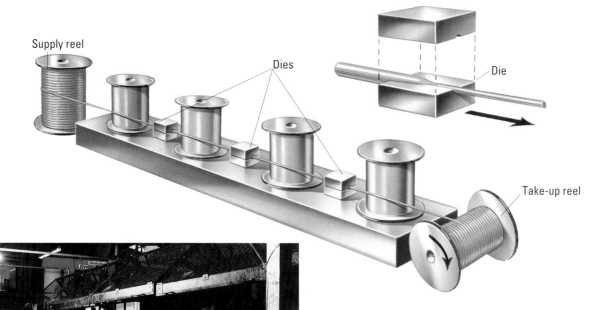

Supply reel

Dies

Die

Take-up reel

WIRE

Wire is made on a machine by a process called drawing (above), in which a rod or thick wire is pulled through a series of dies until the desired thickness is reached.

series of holes in a process called drawing. Each hole is in a tool called a die and is smaller than the one before it (see DIE). The metal is passed through the holes until the desired thickness is reached. It is then wound around a drum for storage and transport.

Drawing the wire increases the strength of the metal. Thus, a cable made up of several strands of wire bundled together is actually stronger than a single rod of metal of the same thickness as the cable (see CABLE).

Wire has a variety of uses. For example, suspension bridges are held up by giant cables made of thousands of wires (see BRIDGE). Telephone lines and electric power lines are long, thin wires. Short lengths of wire are used to make nails, paper clips, pins, and staples. Varying lengths of wire are used to make fences and strings for musical instruments, such as guitars and pianos.

WISTERIA (wĭ stîr′ē ə) *Wisteria* is a genus of climbing shrubs belonging to the pea family. Best known of the six species is Chinese wisteria, which grows on many buildings in the United States. It is

WISTERIA

Wisteria, a climbing plant of the pea family, has hanging clusters of bluish violet flowers.

a vigorous plant, and one individual is reported to have covered almost 1,000 sq. ft. [93 sq. m] of wall space. Chinese wisteria has clusters of sweetly scented bluish violet flowers. The flower clusters are from 1 to 2 ft. [30 to 61 cm] long. Wisteria pods and seeds contain a poison that can cause severe stomach pain if they are eaten.

See also CLIMBING PLANT; PEA FAMILY.

WITCH HAZEL FAMILY

The witch hazel family (Hamamelidaceae) includes about 30 genera (plural of *genus*) and 100 species of trees and shrubs that live in tropical and temperate areas throughout the world. They have simple leaves and clusters of

WITCH HAZEL FAMILY
Chinese witch hazel is a shrub (below) that bears masses of small yellow flowers (right). It blooms in winter when there are no leaves on the shrub.

small flowers. The fruits are dry and woody (see CLIMATE; LEAF; SHRUB; TREE).

American witch hazel grows in the eastern United States and Canada. Its forked twigs were once used as rods that were supposed to be able to locate underground water. This and other superstitions led to the plant's name. Like many other witch hazels, it has spiky flowers, with narrow petals, that open in winter when there are no leaves on the trees. The bark and leaves can be distilled in alcohol to produce witch hazel lotion (see DISTILLATION). This lotion is used to treat bruises, inflammation, and other skin problems.

WOLF

The wolf is a carnivorous (meat-eating) mammal closely related to the domestic dog and the coyote (see COYOTE; DOG; MAMMAL). Wolves are found in the wilderness areas of Asia, Europe, and North America, including Greenland. The animals have a fairly broad head, powerful jaws, and short ears. The ears always stand erect. Male wolves generally weigh more than 100 lb. [45 kg]. Females often weigh less.

The two main species of wolf are the gray wolf and the red wolf, although zoologists are not sure that they are really separate species. Gray wolves are so called because of their thick, gray fur. The Arctic wolf, which is a kind of gray wolf, may be pure white. The red wolf, which lives in the southern United States and is now extremely rare, gets its name from its reddish fur.

Wolves usually have strong family units. Wolf families, called wolf packs, remain together for long periods. A wolf uses its howl to tell other wolves of its presence. The howling sound helps keep the pack together.

Female wolves have a gestation period of about two months (see GESTATION PERIOD). A litter usually consists of four to seven babies called pups.

Wolves were once the most widely distributed of all wild mammals, but they are now endangered in most areas. Farmers and ranchers have killed many wolves because the animals sometimes attack livestock. Many people are afraid of wolves,

WOLF

Wolves have been hunted to near extinction over much of their native range. Shown here are (1) the European gray wolf, (2) the Tibetan gray wolf, and (3) a gray wolf/husky dog cross.

though the animals would rather stay away from human beings.

See also ENDANGERED SPECIES.

WOLVERINE (wo͝ool′və rēn′) The wolverine is probably the largest member of the weasel family, Mustelidae. It is related to badgers, skunks, and otters. However, the wolverine looks like a small bear with a long tail. The animal is sometimes called "the glutton" because it has an enormous appetite. It eats various small mammals and birds. However, it feeds largely on animals, such as deer, that have been killed by other carnivores (meat eaters). The wolverine frequently kills more

WOLVERINE

The wolverine—also known as "the glutton" because of its large appetite—looks like a small bear with a long tail. Its coat is dark and shaggy, with tan markings.

animals than it can eat. The wolverine often buries uneaten food or carries it up into a tree for safekeeping.

Wolverines have a body length of about 2.5 ft. [76 cm]. The animal's coat consists of dark, shaggy hair with tan markings.

Wolverines once roamed the northern woods of Asia, Europe, and North America. The animals are rare today because they have been hunted extensively for their fur.

See also WEASEL.

WOMBAT

The wombat is a nocturnal marsupial native to Australia and Tasmania. It is closely related to the koala.

WOMBAT (wŏm′băt′) The wombat, sometimes called the Australian badger, is a thickly built marsupial (see MARSUPIAL). Wombats are found in southern Australia and the nearby island of Tasmania. The animal's fur is often grayish brown or a yellowish black. The wombat is about 3 ft. [91 cm] long and weighs up to 80 lb. [36 kg].

The wombat's strong, short legs are used to dig out the long burrows in which it lives. The female's pouch opens to the rear, so that it does not get full of dirt when the animal is burrowing. Wombats are nocturnal (active at night). They leave their burrows to feed on grass and other plants (see NOCTURNAL BEHAVIOR).

The fur of the wombat has been used to make long-wearing rugs. Some people keep wombats as pets.

WOOD Wood is the tough, nonliving part of trees and shrubs beneath the bark. It is mostly cellulose and makes up the greatest part of a fully grown tree (see BARK; CELLULOSE; SHRUB; TREE; WOODY PLANT). There are two layers of wood: sapwood and heartwood. The sapwood is located just under the bark. It contains the younger xylem, which carries water and dissolved minerals from the roots to the leaves (see XYLEM). The heartwood, in the center of the trunk or branch, is made up of older xylem. Heartwood is heavier and darker than sapwood because it contains gums, resins, and tannin, a reddish coloring agent (see HEARTWOOD; RESIN; SAPWOOD).

The pattern found in wood is called the figure. It contains marks such as growth rings, knurls, and

WOOD

Wood has hundreds of different uses. Here workers in Thailand are sawing teak logs into planks for making furniture.

knots. Growth rings are thin, wavy, dark-colored lines in the wood that show the tree's annual growth (see ANNUAL RING). Knurls and knots are small dark-colored circular marks that are places where branches once were located. Some woods also contain light and dark streaks in the heartwood known as pigment figures (see PIGMENT).

There are hardwoods, such as oak, and softwoods, such as pine. Almost 50 percent of all wood cut in the United States is made into lumber (see LUMBER). Another 34 percent is ground into wood pulp to make paper. The remainder is used to make furniture, veneers (wood layers), plywoods, poles, posts, pilings, and home heating fuel.

WOOD LOUSE

Wood lice (plural of *wood louse*), also called sow bugs, are small land-living crustaceans distantly related to crabs and lobsters. They belong to the order Isopoda. There are hundreds of species, and their domed, oval bodies are usually gray or brown. They have seven pairs of identical legs. *Isopoda* means "equal feet." Wood lice are the only group of crustaceans that live mainly on land, but they still have to live in damp places. They live in leaf litter, under loose bark, and

WOOD LOUSE
The wood louse is the only common crustacean that lives entirely out of water. It can be found under stones, in old wood, and in the bark of trees.

under logs and stones. They feed mainly on decaying plant matter, including rotting wood. Some species can roll themselves into balls when alarmed. They also roll up in dry weather, as this cuts down the amount of water lost from their bodies.

The gribble is a marine relative of the wood louse that destroys the timbers of ships and jetties. *See also* CRUSTACEAN.

WOODPECKER

A woodpecker is a bird that belongs to the family Picidae. It is called a woodpecker because it pecks into wood, looking for insects to eat. The bill of the bird is long and

WOODPECKER
The woodpecker family includes flickers and sapsuckers. Pictured here are (1) a yellow-bellied sapsucker, (2) a pileated woodpecker (*pileated* means "crested"), and (3) a common flicker.

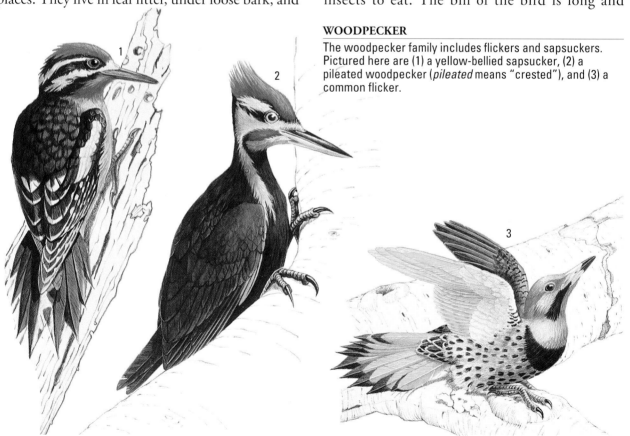

strong. It has a chisellike tip to help it drill holes into trees—usually, those that are dead or unhealthy. The woodpecker then uses its long tongue to capture and eat the insects living inside these trees.

There are more than twenty species of woodpeckers found in North America. These include the flickers and sapsuckers (see SAPSUCKER). There is much variation in size among woodpeckers. The downy woodpecker, common through much of the continent, is only about 5.5 in. [14 cm] long. The pileated woodpecker, found in the eastern and northwestern United States and in parts of Canada, can reach a length of 15 in. [38 cm]. Most woodpeckers nest in large holes they make in the branches or trunks of trees.
See also BIRD.

WOODS, GRANVILLE T. (1856–1910)
Granville T. Woods was an inventor who was granted more than fifty patents. A patent is a document issued by a government. It grants a person exclusive rights to an invention for a period of time.

Woods, an African-American, was born in Columbus, Ohio. He took some college engineering courses, but he was mostly self-taught. As an adult, Woods worked in a machine shop and as a railway engineer. He patented his most important invention, the synchronous multiplex railway telegraph, in 1887. This invention made rail traffic safer because it allowed crews on different moving trains to communicate with each other and with rail stations (see RAILROAD; TELEGRAPH). Wood's other inventions include a kind of air brake, a kind of battery, an egg incubator (warmer), and various kinds of telegraph equipment.
See also INVENTION.

WOODY PLANT
A woody plant is either a shrub or a tree. It has one or more hard, stiff stems that contain large amounts of xylem. The walls of the cells that make up the xylem are thickened with cellulose and lignin, two substances that add great strength to the cells. There are also many woody fibers stretching throughout the plant. All woody plants are perennial.
See also CELLULOSE; HERBACEOUS PLANT; LIGNIN; PERENNIAL PLANT; SHRUB; STEM; TREE; WOOD; XYLEM.

WOODY PLANT
Trees and shrubs (above) are woody plants. The stems are hard, stiff, and fibrous, as can be seen in the split tree branch (left).

WOOL
Wool is a fiber that usually comes from the protective covering, or fleece, of sheep. Similar fibers are obtained from various breeds of goats and alpacas (see FIBER). The quality of wool depends on the age and physical condition of the sheep and the climate in which it lives. The fleece of a healthy sheep is covered by yolk. Yolk is an oily substance consisting of grease and dried perspiration. Yolk protects the sheep from rain. It also keeps the fleece from becoming matted or tangled. Young sheep produce the best wool. Very old or diseased sheep produce low-quality wool.

The processing of wool involves four main steps. The first is shearing, or clipping. Most sheep

shearers use power shears. Experts can shear two hundred or more animals a day. The second step involves grading and sorting. Workers remove any stained or damaged wool from each fleece. They then sort the rest of the wool according to the quality of the fibers. Wool fibers are judged by their strength, fineness, length, waviness, and color. The third step is concerned with making yarn. After the wool is cleaned and dried, it is carded. Carding involves passing the wool through rollers that have thin wire teeth. The teeth untangle the fibers and arrange them into a flat sheet called a web. The web is formed into narrow ropes called slivers. The slivers are stretched into thinner strands called rovings. Spinning machines twist the rovings into yarn. Yarn called woolen yarn is bulky and fuzzy. Worsted yarn is smooth and highly twisted.

The fourth and final step involves making fabric. Wool manufacturers knit or weave yarn into a variety of fabrics. Woolen yarns are used in making flannel and tweed fabrics. Worsted yarns are used for fabrics such as gabardine, sharkskin, and twill.

Wool may be dyed at various stages of the manufacturing process. All wool fabrics undergo finishing processes to give them a certain look and feel. *See also* DYE; SHEEP; TEXTILE.

WORK If a force moves an object, work is said to be done by the force (see FORCE). For instance, work is done when a force is used to lift an object upward. On the other hand, work is not done if an object is held steadily at arm's length because the force does not move the object. The work done when a force moves an object is measured by the product of the force and the amount of movement produced in the direction of the force.

Energy is needed to do work (see ENERGY). When a force moves an object, the object gains energy. The amount of energy gained by the object equals the amount of work done on the object by the force.

In the customary system of measurements, which is used in the United States, the unit of work and energy is the foot-pound. One foot-pound is the work done or the energy used by a force of one pound through a distance of one foot. The unit used to measure work and energy in the metric system is the joule (see JOULE). One joule is the work done or the energy used by a force of one newton moving a distance of one meter. The rate of doing work is called power (see POWER). The unit of power in the metric system is the watt (see WATT). One watt is one joule per second. A unit used to measure the power of engines is horsepower, which equals 746 watts (see HORSEPOWER).

WORM *Worm* is the common name given to a wide range of slender animals. The true worms all lack backbones. They belong to four main groups. These are the Annelida, or segmented worms; the Aschelminthes, or roundworms; the Nemertea, or ribbon worms; and the Platyhelminthes, or flat-worms (see ANNELIDA; INVERTEBRATE; NEMATODE; PLATYHELMINTHES). The caterpillars of some moths are also called worms, although they have legs (see WEBWORM).

The best-known worms are the annelids, or segmented worms, whose bodies are divided into

numerous rings and segments. They include the bristleworms, leeches, and earthworms (see EARTHWORM; LEECH). Some earthworms are over 10 ft. [3 m] long, and some marine ribbon worms are over 65 ft. [20 m] long. There are also roundworms that cannot be seen without a micro-scope. Many worms live as parasites inside other animals, including human beings, and also in plants (see PARASITE). Flukes, tapeworms, and pinworms are among the parasites of human beings (see TAPEWORM). 🔬 PROJECT 75

WREN A wren is a small bird that belongs to the family Troglodytidae. It is mostly brown with a long, thin bill. The wren often hops from branch to branch with its tail tilted upward.

There are several species of wrens in North America. They are found in many types of habitats, including deserts, forests, marshes, and meadows. Wrens eat insects and are known for their loud and pretty songs. Most wrens are between 3 and 4.75 in. [7.5 and 11.7 cm] in length, but the cactus wren is about 6.5 in. [16.5 cm] long.
See also BIRD.

WORM

Worms are soft, slender animals. Shown here are (1) a polychaete worm, (2) a ragworm, and (3) another polychaete worm. All belong to the Annelida group.

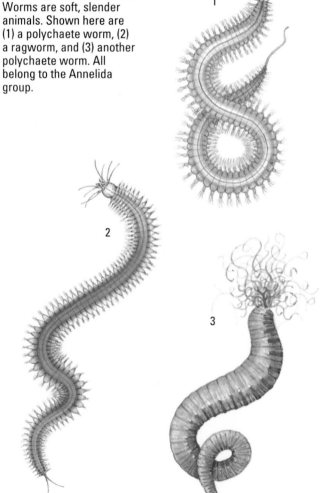

WREN

Wrens are birds known for their small size and tuneful songs. They include the house wren (above) and the winter wren (left).

WRIGHT BROTHERS Wilbur (1867–1912) and Orville (1871–1948) Wright—the Wright brothers—invented, built, and flew the first powered airplane. The world's first flight in a heavier-than-air, power-driven machine occurred in December 17, 1903, at Kitty Hawk, North Carolina. Orville won the toss of a coin and had the

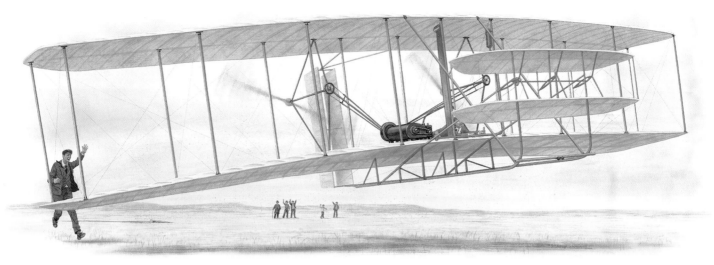

WRIGHT BROTHERS

The Wright brothers' first successful airplane—called the *Flyer* (above)—had a small gasoline engine that they designed themselves. It first flew in December 1903, piloted by Orville (on left of the photograph below). He continued their pioneering work on his own after his brother, Wilbur (on the right), died in 1912.

honor of piloting the airplane on its first flight. He flew 120 ft. [37 m] and remained in the air for twelve seconds. Three more flights were made that day. The longest flight was by Wilbur at 852 ft. [260 m] in fifty-nine seconds.

The flights were scarcely noticed by the world.

Only three or four newspapers reported them the next day, and those reports were inaccurate. The Wright brothers themselves could not have foreseen how the airplane would change civilization. The brothers built that first plane for less than $1,000. Its two wings were 40.5 ft. [12 m] long each. It weighed about 750 lb. [340 kg], including the weight of the pilot. A small gasoline engine of their own design drove a pair of two-bladed propellers (see ENGINE; PROPELLER).

The Wrights continued to experiment with airplanes after 1903. Wilbur went to France in 1908 and made flights to altitudes of 295 ft. [90 m] and more. In Virginia, Orville made fifty-seven complete circles at an altitude of 120 ft. [37 m]. In 1912, Wilbur died of typhoid fever, and Orville continued to work alone. In 1916, he opened the Wright Aeronautical Laboratory and was a pioneer in many developments in aviation. In 1929, Orville accepted the Daniel Guggenheim Medal for Wilbur's and his contributions to aviation. Today, the original plane used at Kitty Hawk hangs in the National Air and Space Museum in Washington, D.C.

See also AIRPLANE; AVIATION.

WROUGHT IRON (rôt ī′ərn) Wrought iron is a very pure form of iron (see IRON). It is made by purifying molten (melted) pig iron. Pig iron is a type of iron that is made in a blast furnace (see BLAST FURNACE; PIG IRON). The pig iron is purified in a special furnace called a puddling furnace. The furnace is made so that heat is reflected from a special lining to the iron. The high temperature removes impurities such as carbon, phosphorus, silicon, and sulfur. The wrought iron that is made contains less than 0.3 percent carbon. The metal is malleable (readily hammered into shape) and ductile (easily pulled out into rods or wires). The wrought iron contains 1 to 3 percent of impurities called slag. The slag content makes the iron more resistant to corrosion than ordinary iron (see CORROSION). Wrought iron was once widely used on its own. However, most wrought iron is now made into steel. *See also* STEEL.

WU, CHIEN-SHIUNG (wōō, chyĕn-shŭng)

(1912–) Chien-shiung Wu is a Chinese-American physicist. She is best known for performing an experiment at Columbia University in New York City in 1957 to support a theory developed by physicists Tsung Dao Lee and Chen Ning Yang (see LEE, TSUNG DAO; YANG, CHEN NING). Lee's and Yang's theory suggested that a long-accepted law of physics was not always true (see PHYSICS). This law, called the law of conservation of parity, says there is no way to tell whether something is an event or a mirror image of the event because both satisfy laws of nature. Wu's experiment found that electrons moving at very low temperatures sometimes have distinct patterns and are not mirror images of each other (see ELECTRON). Lee and Yang were awarded the Nobel Prize for physics in 1957 for their theory, but Wu's contributions were overlooked.

Wu was born in China. She received a bachelor's degree from the National Central University in Nanking, China, in 1934. In 1936, she moved to the United States and received a doctoral degree in physics from the University of California at Berkeley. She then worked with the Manhattan Project at Columbia University in New York City. The Manhattan Project involved a group of scientists who developed the atomic bomb, which was used in World War II (1939–1945) (see NUCLEAR WEAPONS). Wu's other contributions to science include a method for producing large quantities of uranium atoms that are able to split in an atomic reaction. Up until then, it was difficult for scientists to produce large quantities of uranium atoms. Wu

also improved existing Geiger counters and conducted research to help find a cure for sickle cell anemia using nuclear physics (see GEIGER COUNTER; NUCLEAR ENERGY; SICKLE CELL ANEMIA).

X

X CHROMOSOME
Human body cells contain 23 pairs of chromosomes (see CHROMOSOME). The X chromosome is one of the pair that determines a person's sex. If a person has a pair of X chromosomes, she will be female. If a person has one X chromosome and one Y chromosome, he will be male (see Y CHROMOSOME).

The X chromosome is much larger than the Y chromosome. It contains the genetic information that determines female characteristics, but it also contains much more genetic information than the Y chromosome does. For example, color blindness is determined by a recessive gene carried on the X chromosome (see COLOR BLINDNESS; GENE; RECESSIVE

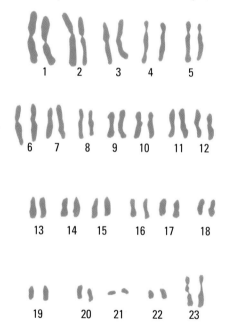

X CHROMOSOME

Geneticists (scientists who study genetics) sometimes cut up photographs of human chromosomes and arrange them in numbered pairs. Pair number 23 in the above set are both X chromosomes, showing that the set belongs to a female.

CHARACTER). The Y chromosome carries no gene for color vision. If a female receives a recessive gene for color blindness and a dominant gene for color vision, she will not be color blind (see DOMINANCE). A male, however, receives only one gene that controls color vision, the one on the X chromosome. This means that if he receives a recessive gene for color blindness from his mother, he will be color blind. Therefore, color blindness is a sex-linked trait. Hemophilia is a disease that is sex linked as well (see HEMOPHILIA).

Some diseases are caused by a person having too many X chromosomes. The individual usually shows signs of poor physical and mental development. Often, the individual is sterile (cannot have children). *See also* GENETICS; HEREDITY.

XANTHOPHYLL (zăn'thə fĭl´) Xanthophyll, or lutein, is a yellowish orange pigment (coloring substance) found in plants, egg yolks, and some algae. It is an organic (carbon-containing) compound with the chemical formula $C_{40}H_{56}O_2$ (see COMPOUND). Xanthophyll exists in large amounts in many leaves where, with the green pigment chlorophyll, it plays a role in photosynthesis (see CHLOROPHYLL; PHOTOSYNTHESIS). Leaves are usually green because the chlorophyll masks the

xanthophyll. In the fall, however, the chlorophyll begins to decrease, and the xanthophyll shows through. This gives the leaves a yellow or orange color. Xanthophyll also gives color to some algae, especially the brown seaweeds, and to the yellow petals of many flowers.
See also ALGAE; CAROTENE; PIGMENT.

XEROGRAPHY (zĭ rŏg'rə fē) Xerography is a means of copying documents and illustrations. Its name comes from Greek words meaning "dry writing." Instead of liquid ink, xerography uses static electricity and a dry, light-sensitive substance, such as the element selenium (see ELECTROSTATICS; ELEMENT).

To copy a document or illustration using xerography, the document or illustration is placed face down on a horizontal piece of glass that is part of a xerographic machine. When the machine is started, a bright light shines from beneath the glass onto the document or illustration. The lighter parts of the document, such as blank areas, reflect (bounce back) light. The darker parts of the document, such as words, absorb light rather than reflect it. The light that is reflected passes through a lens. The lens focuses it onto a device, such as a belt, drum, or plate (see LENS). The device has been coated with a

XANTHOPHYLL
The orange-red color of the leaves of this sweet gum tree is due to the pigment xanthophyll.

XEROGRAPHY
A modern photocopier uses the principles of xerography to make black-and-white or colored copies of documents.

light-sensitive substance and has received charges of static electricity (see CHARGE).

The areas on the device hit by light lose their charge. The areas on the device not hit by light keep their charge. The device is then covered with a negatively charged, powdered ink called toner. The toner clings to the parts of the device that have a charge. In this way, an image of the document or illustration is formed in powdered ink on the device.

A sheet of paper passes next to the device. The paper has a positive charge, which attracts the toner from the device. The paper, which now contains the image, is heated before it leaves the machine. This makes the toner melt and stick permanently to the paper.

Xerographic copying was invented by the American scientist John Chester Carlson in 1937. Xerographic, or photocopying, machines are now standard equipment in nearly all offices. Xerographic technology has advanced to include high-speed copying, the making of enlargements or reductions of documents and illustrations, color copying of color originals, and automatic sorting and stapling of copies.

XEROPHYTE (zîr′ə fīt′) Xerophytes are plants that are specially adapted so that they can live in dry places such as deserts (see ADAPTATION). Deserts cover about 20 percent of the land on

XEROPHYTE

Xerophytes are plants whose special adaptations enable them to survive in dry places. Shown here are sea holly (top left), growing in a coastal sand dune, and an aloe (top right), which grows in deserts and stores water in its fleshy leaves. The barrel cactus (left) stores water in its prickly stems.

Earth. Some deserts, such as parts of the Sahara in Africa, have hardly any plant life. In most deserts, though, there is a variety of plants, though they may be small and widely separated. Members of the cactus family are good examples of xerophytes (see CACTUS FAMILY).

Most xerophytes have extensive, spreading roots near the surface of the ground so they can absorb as much water as possible after even a light rainfall. Xerophytes usually have thick, protective cuticles and small, often highly modified, leaves (see CUTICLE; LEAF). The stomata are usually few in number and are somehow shielded or protected from the sun and wind. Many xerophytes have thick stems or other modified structures for storing water.

Some plants that grow in dry places are not true xerophytes. Some desert plants grow quickly after a heavy rain. They scatter seeds before the sand dries and they die. Some desert shrubs have long roots that reach down to underground water supplies, so they do not need special water-saving devices. *See also* PLANT KINGDOM.

X RAY X rays are a form of electromagnetic radiation. They are members of the same family as light waves, gamma rays, and radio waves (see ELECTROMAGNETIC RADIATION). X rays have a much greater frequency than light waves and are invisible.

However, their frequency is less than that of gamma rays, which are also invisible (see FREQUENCY). X rays have many important uses in medicine and other branches of science.

X rays were discovered by the German physicist Wilhelm Conrad Roentgen (also written Röntgen) in 1895. He did not know what they were, and so he called them X rays, because *x* is a scientific symbol for an unknown quantity (see ROENTGEN, WILHELM CONRAD).

X rays are produced when electrons traveling at high speed are sent crashing into a solid material. As they collide with atoms in this target material, the fast-moving electrons slow down, and some of their energy is changed into X rays. Some of the electrons also knock electrons in the atoms of the target material out of their normal positions. This causes the release of energy in the form of X rays (see ATOM; ELECTRON). An X-ray tube is a vacuum tube in which a heated cathode is used to produce electrons (see VACUUM TUBE). The electrons are sped up by means of a high voltage until they strike the anode, which is the target (see VOLT). X rays are produced at the anode, traveling in all directions. Lead shielding around the tube prevents X rays from emerging in any direction other than the beam "port," a hole in the shielding.

Different ranges of X rays of various frequencies

X RAY

Modern X-ray equipment includes scanners, which do not expose a patient to high doses of X rays.

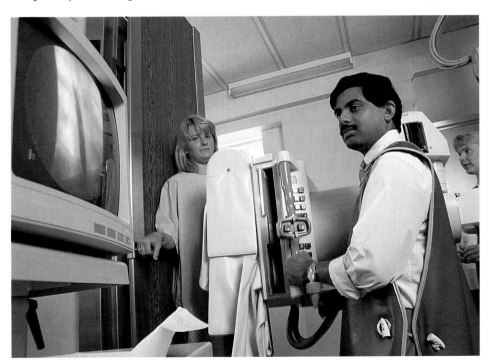

can be produced by changing the voltage that speeds the electrons or the substance of which the target anode is made. When there is a mixture of different X-ray frequencies, the X rays are said to be "white" radiation. X rays that have very high frequencies are called "hard" radiation, and X rays with lower frequencies are called "soft" radiation.

The best-known property of X rays is their ability to pass through many forms of matter. Other properties include the way in which they ionize gases when they pass through them and the way in which they cause fluorescent materials to glow (see IONS AND IONIZATION; FLUORESCENCE). X rays also affect photographic film.

X rays passing into dense materials are absorbed more readily than X rays passing into lighter materials. For this reason, X rays have been used in medicine almost since the time of their discovery. They can be used to show up different internal structures and reveal broken bones or foreign objects in the tissues (see RADIOGRAPHY; TOMOGRAPHY).

Large doses of X rays have a damaging effect on the body's cells. They can be used to destroy unwanted cells in the body and are therefore useful for the treatment of cancer. However, they must be used under carefully controlled conditions (see RADIATION THERAPY).

In physics, the use of X rays helps reveal the structure of various kinds of substances, especially crystals.

XYLEM (zī'ləm) Xylem is the tissue that carries water and dissolved minerals from the roots to the leaves of vascular plants. It is a system of tubes made up of dead cells with thick, woody walls. These walls have large amounts of cellulose and lignin (see CELLULOSE; LIGNIN). Xylem is surrounded by many fibers that extend along its length. This structure gives a great deal of support to the plant. Tree trunks consist almost entirely of xylem.

In ferns and gymnosperms, xylem is made of tapering, tube-shaped cells called tracheids. The walls of the tracheids have many tiny pits, or holes, to allow water and dissolved minerals to pass from one cell to the next. In angiosperms, however,

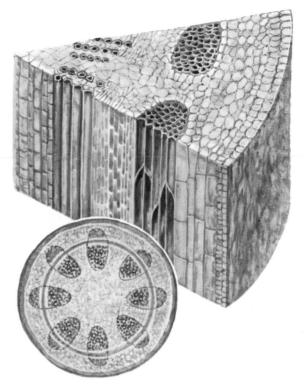

XYLEM

A segment of a small tree branch (top) shows the tubes of xylem that carry water and dissolved minerals from the roots to the leaves of the plant. The small cross section (bottom) of a one-year-old twig shows how xylem develops inward from the cambium (inner ring), which is the main living tissue of the tree trunk and branches.

xylem is made of long, tubular vessels. These vessels are made of cells whose ends have disintegrated, leaving a continuous tube.

See also VASCULAR PLANT; WOOD.

Y

Y CHROMOSOME Human body cells contain 23 pairs of chromosomes (see CHROMOSOME). The Y chromosome is one of the two chromosomes that determine a person's sex, along with the X chromosome (see X CHROMOSOME). If a person has a pair of X chromosomes, she will be female. If a person has only one X chromosome and one Y chromosome, he will be male. The Y chromosome contains the genetic information that determines male characteristics and ensures that the testes develop in the growing baby in the uterus (womb) (see TESTICLE). *See also* GENE; GENETICS; HEREDITY.

YAK The yak is a shaggy wild ox found in Asia, especially in the mountains of Tibet. It can live at 20,000 ft. [6,000 m], which is higher than any other mammal. The yak stands about 6 ft. [1.8 m] at the shoulder. The animal weighs from 1,100 to 1,200 lb. [499 to 544 kg]. Yaks are covered with black or brownish hair. The hair is very long and silky.

Although the yak is heavily built, it is quite agile. It can slide down icy slopes, swim rivers, and cross steep rock slides. If forced to defend itself, a yak can make a powerful charge. Many wild yaks have been killed by hunters and truly wild yaks now exist only on the highest and wildest mountains. The animal is now in danger of extinction (see EXTINCTION).

The yak has been domesticated. The domesticated yak is often called the grunting ox. It is the result of many generations of careful breeding (see BREEDING). It is usually white or spotted. Domesticated yaks are smaller than the wild ones.

YAK

The yak is a large and thickly built animal. However, yaks are very agile, moving easily about the mountainous areas of their habitat. If forced to defend themselves, yaks can make a powerful charge.

The domesticated ones are often used as pack animals. Also, their hair is used to make cloth and mats. Saddles, boots, and other articles are made from the hides.

YAM The yam is a vegetable that is often confused with the sweet potato (see SWEET POTATO). It belongs to the family Dioscoreaceae. The plant's tubers (swollen underground stems) are full of starch and they are a major food source in many tropical areas (see TUBER). The plant has climbing stems that bear small, green flower clusters.

Most of the world's yam crop is grown in western Africa. India, southeast Asia, and the West Indies are other areas where yams are important crops. Some yams are grown in the southern part of the United States.

YAM

The starchy tubers of the yam are a popular food in tropical parts of the world.

YANG, CHEN NING (1922–) Chen Ning Yang is a Chinese-American physicist. He is best known for his work with Tsung Dao Lee and Chien-shiung Wu (see LEE, TSUNG DAO; WU, CHIEN-SHIUNG). Yang and Lee developed a theory that suggested that a long-accepted law of physics was not always true (see PHYSICS). This law, called the law of conservation of parity, says there is no way to tell whether something is an event or a mirror image of the event because both satisfy laws of nature. However, Lee and Yang said that there is a difference between the event and the image in certain nuclear reactions (see NUCLEAR ENERGY). Wu performed the actual experiment that proved their theory in 1957. Lee and Yang were awarded the Nobel Prize for physics in 1957.

Yang was born in China. He received his bachelor's degree from the National Southwest Associated University in Kunming, China. He earned a master's degree in physics at Tsinghua University at Kunming. Yang then attended the University of Chicago in the United States. There, he studied with Enrico Fermi (see FERMI, ENRICO). Yang received his doctoral degree in 1948. He then joined the Institute for Advanced Study in Princeton, New Jersey. The institute is a research center for those scientists who have already received a doctoral degree. It was while he was researching at the institute that Yang developed his Nobel-Prize-winning theory with Lee. In 1955, Yang became professor of physics at the State University of New York at Stony Brook. He became a member of the National Academy of Sciences in 1965. The academy conducts scientific research and advises the United States government about scientific matters.

YEAR A year is the time it takes the earth to make one complete revolution around the sun. Several different types of years are recognized. These include astronomical years, which are used in astronomy and are based on the movement of the earth around the sun, and calendar years, in which the beginning, subdivisions, and length of the year are fixed (see ASTRONOMY; CALENDAR).

The most important and widely used astronomical year is the tropical year, also known as the solar or equinoctial year. This is the time interval between occurrences of the spring equinox, the date in March (in the Northern Hemisphere) when the sun is directly over the equator and day and night are of equal length (see EQUINOX). The tropical year now lasts about 365.2422 days, but its length is decreasing very slowly as the result of small changes in the speed of the earth's rotation and its orbit around the sun.

In everyday life, people generally rely on the Gregorian solar calendar year. In this calendar, most years have 365 days, but leap years, which occur every four years, have 366 days, with an extra day in February.

YEAST *Yeast* is the common name for about 160 types of one-celled fungi (see FUNGUS). Yeasts reproduce quickly, both asexually by budding or fission and sexually by producing gametes that join to form a zygote (see REPRODUCTION). Yeasts feed on sugar and, in the absence of air, convert it into carbon dioxide (a gas) and alcohol. For this reason, yeasts are used in making many types of breads and alcoholic beverages.

In baking, yeasts are used to make the dough rise. Some of the enzymes produced by the yeasts convert starch in the flour into sugar (see ENZYME). Other enzymes from the yeasts change this sugar into carbon dioxide and alcohol (see FERMENTATION). The carbon dioxide forms bubbles that cause the dough to increase in size, or rise. Because these enzymes work only within a limited temperature range—about 80° to 85°F [27° to 29°C]—the dough must be kept warm in order to rise. When the dough is baked, the alcohol evaporates, and the yeasts are killed. As a result, baked bread does not have any yeast or alcohol taste.

Yeasts are present in the air almost everywhere. In the past, bakers collected yeasts by leaving a mixture of flour, sugar, and water uncovered for a few hours. Although some people still use this method, most prefer to buy commercially prepared yeasts. Yeasts are sold in grocery stores in two forms: dry and compressed. Dry yeast is inactive yeast cells. It

YEAST

In brewing, yeast converts sugar into alcohol and carbon dioxide gas. The gas rises to the top of the vat and converts the surface liquid into a foam.

can be stored indefinitely and is activated by adding warm water and sugar (or starch). Compressed yeast, however, contains active yeast cells, moisture, and starch. Compressed yeast lasts for a relatively short time and must be kept refrigerated until used.

YELLOW FEVER Yellow fever (or yellow jack) is a disease caused by a virus (see VIRUS). The disease damages many tissues in the human body, especially the liver. Such damage makes the liver unable to work properly. As a result, the skin appears yellow, giving the disease its name. Walter Reed, a United States Army physician, proved that yellow fever is spread by a mosquito. This theory had first been put forth by the Cuban physician Carlos Finlay. Three research physicians later proved that the microorganism carried by the mosquito is a virus (see FINLAY, CARLOS; MICROORGANISM; REED, WALTER).

In most cases, a type of mosquito carries the yellow fever virus from one person to another. A mosquito infected with the virus can transmit the disease for the rest of its life.

Symptoms of yellow fever include fever, headache, dizziness, and muscle pain. If the disease progresses beyond this stage, the skin may turn yellow. The victim bleeds from the gums and stomach lining. Some patients go into a coma (see COMA). Death may follow the coma. About 3 percent of all cases of yellow fever result in death

Yellow fever can be prevented with a vaccine developed in 1937 by Max Theiler, a South African research physician.
See also VACCINATION.

YEW (yoo) Yews are evergreen trees and shrubs that belong to the genus *Taxus* of the family Taxaceae (see EVERGREEN). Yews have dark green, needlelike leaves arranged in spirals on the spreading branches. They are classified as conifers, and the male trees scatter pollen from little yellow cone-like structures. Female trees do not form cones, however. They bear their seeds singly in fleshy red cups called arils. The bark, leaves, and seeds, but not the arils, are poisonous.

There are seven species of yews, and they all grow

in temperate areas of the Northern Hemisphere. The trees often grow to a height of 80 ft. [25 m]. They grow slowly and may live for hundreds of years. Yew wood is hard and beautifully grained. It is used in making fine furniture, archery bows, and small carved objects.

YEW

Yew trees have needlelike leaves and rough, stringy bark. The seeds are carried in fleshy cups called arils. All parts of the plant, except the arils, are poisonous.

YUCCA Yuccas are a group of plants native to Mexico and the southern and southwestern United States. Yuccas belong to the agave family, Agavaceae, and there are about 30 species.

Although some yucca plants are almost stemless, some have stems 33 ft. [10 m] high. The sword-shaped leaves grow in clusters at the tip of the stem. The bell-shaped flowers range in color from whitish green to white to cream. The flowers grow on a tall stem arising from the center of a leaf cluster. The flowers emit a strong odor when they open at night. The yucca fruit contains many black seeds.

Yuccas can only be pollinated by a certain group of moths. Each species of yucca moth can only pollinate a certain species of yucca (see POLLINATION).

Yuccas were used by Native Americans for many purposes. For example, they ate the buds and flowers and made rope, mats, and baskets from the leaf fibers.

Z

ZEBRA The zebra is an African member of the horse family. It is easily recognized by its striped coat. This color pattern makes the zebra different from all other members of the horse family. The parallel black or dark brown stripes on white are arranged in exact designs. The stripes run all over the body, meeting in a diagonal pattern at the head. The stripes help hide the zebra from its enemies by making it blend into the patterns of shadow and sunlight where it lives (see CAMOUFLAGE; PROTECTIVE COLORATION). The lion is the zebra's main enemy.

Zebras are grazing animals. Some kinds of zebras roam open grassy plains. Others live in rough mountains. Zebras live in small bands. Each group is led by a stallion (adult male). Great numbers of zebras have been killed for their meat and hides. Some kinds of zebras are nearly extinct, and others are numerous (see EXTINCTION). Although there is some disagreement about the number of species of zebras, it is generally considered that there are three: the mountain zebra, Burchell's zebra, and Grevy's zebra. Each species has a slightly different stripe pattern, and only Burchell's zebra has stripes on the belly. Burchell's zebras are the most common and can be found over a wide area of eastern and southern Africa. Grevy's zebra is the largest species and lives in the mountains of east Africa. The mountain zebra lives in southwest Africa.

ZEBRA
Burchell's zebra (top) has black stripes across its belly. The mountain zebra (bottom) has narrow hoofs, a smooth coat, and a dewlap at its throat. Its belly is white.

ZENITH The zenith is the point on the celestial sphere directly above an observer. The opposite of the zenith is the nadir.

See also CELESTIAL SPHERE; NADIR.

ZINC Zinc (Zn) is a bluish white metallic element (see ELEMENT). Zinc is never found pure in nature. It often occurs combined with sulfur in a mineral called zinc blende or sphalerite. This ore is found in Britain, Australia, Africa, and the United States. A coating of zinc is often applied to metals, such as iron or steel, to prevent rusting. The coated metal is called galvanized iron or steel. The galvanized metal is used for products such as roof gutters (see GALVANIZING).

Zinc is often combined with other metals to form alloys. Brass is an alloy of copper and zinc. Some bronzes are copper, tin, and zinc. Nickel silver is

ZINC
Zinc is used to rustproof steel in the process called galvanizing. A thin coating of zinc is applied to the steel by electroplating or by dipping it in a bath of molten zinc (above).

copper, nickel, and zinc. Since the 1980s, the United States penny has been made of a zinc alloy thinly coated with copper (see ALLOY; BRASS; BRONZE; NICKEL SILVER).

Moist air discolors zinc with a coating of zinc oxide (ZnO). After a thin layer of this coating forms, the air cannot tarnish the zinc below it. White, powdery zinc oxide is a very useful chemical in industry. It is used in the manufacture of cosmetics, plastic, rubber, and soap. The chemical is also used as a pigment (coloring substance) in paints and inks.

Zinc sulfide (ZnS) is luminescent and is used on luminous dials in clocks and to make luminous paints (see LUMINESCENCE). It is also used to coat the inside of television screens. Zinc chloride ($ZnCl_2$) in a water solution preserves wood from decay and protects it from insects.

Zinc is used in electric batteries. It is also used in solders. Zinc and its alloys are used in die casting, electroplating, and powder metallurgy (see BATTERY; CASTING; POWDER METALLURGY; SOLDERING AND BRAZING).

Zinc also belongs to the group of nutrients known as minerals. Zinc is necessary in the human diet to promote normal growth and development (see DIET; NUTRITION).

The atomic number of zinc is 30. Its relative atomic mass is 65.39. Zinc has a melting point of 787.24°F [419.58°C]. The element boils at 1,664.6°F [907°C].

ZODIAC (zō′dē ăk′) The zodiac is a belt in the heavens that extends on both sides of the ecliptic. The ecliptic is the sun's apparent path through the heavens (see ECLIPTIC). The zodiac is divided into twelve equal parts, called signs, which are named for groups of stars called constellations (see CONSTELLATION). The signs of the zodiac are Aquarius, Aries, Cancer, Capricorn, Gemini, Leo, Libra, Pisces, Sagittarius, Scorpio, Taurus, and Virgo.

Each sign of the zodiac was assigned a certain time period by ancient astronomers. Aries, for example, was assigned March 21 – April 20. These periods corresponded to the times when the sun was in a particular zodiac constellation. However,

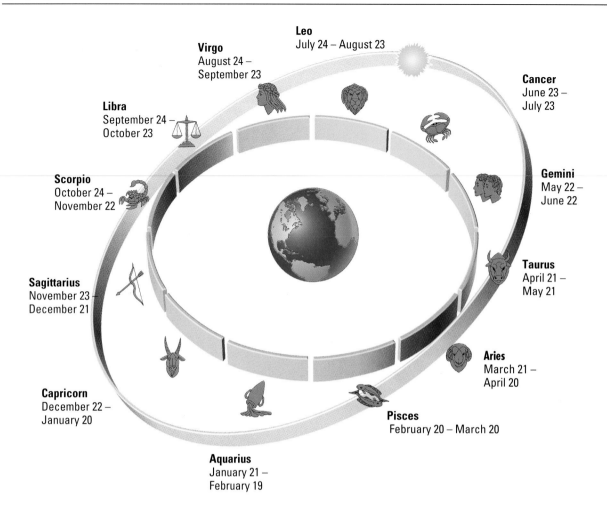

Leo
July 24 – August 23

Virgo
August 24 –
September 23

Libra
September 24 –
October 23

Cancer
June 23 –
July 23

Scorpio
October 24 –
November 22

Gemini
May 22 –
June 22

Sagittarius
November 23 –
December 21

Taurus
April 21 –
May 21

Capricorn
December 22 –
January 20

Aries
March 21 –
April 20

Pisces
February 20 – March 20

Aquarius
January 21 –
February 19

ZODIAC

Each sign of the zodiac was assigned a certain time period by ancient astronomers. These periods corresponded to the times when the sun was in a particular zodiac constellation.

the periods are no longer accurate because of slight changes of the earth's axis (see PRECESSION).

Some people think that the zodiac influences their lives. Such people follow the beliefs of astrology. *See also* ASTROLOGY.

ZOO A zoo, or zoological garden or park, is a place where living animals are kept and displayed. In zoos, people can see and learn about wild animals from throughout the world. Many zoos sponsor special tours, educational activities, and magazines or newsletters. Zoos also serve as "living laboratories," where scientists can study the body structure and function and the behavior of animals. In recent years, zoos have played an important role in wildlife conservation, particularly for rare or endangered species (see CONSERVATION; ENDANGERED SPECIES).

Types of zoos There are more than 600 zoos throughout the world. Most are located in or near large cities. Some large zoos have thousands of wild animals—including mammals, birds, reptiles, amphibians, fish, and insects—from throughout the world. The world's largest zoo in terms of number of animals, the San Diego Zoo in California, has more than 3,200 animals representing about 800 species. Most zoos have a more limited, though worldwide, collection. Some zoos specialize in one group of animals. The Arizona-Sonora Desert Museum in Tucson, Arizona, for example, exhibits only animals that live in the Sonora Desert. The New England Aquarium in Boston, Massachusetts, has more than 450 species of fish on display.

Children's zoos throughout the country allow children (and adults) to see and actually touch tame animals. Although most of these animals are domestic animals, such as goats, some children's zoos also have baby wild animals, such as elephants and monkeys.

Since the 1960s, drive-through, or safari, zoos have

become popular. In these zoos, animals wander freely through large, open areas. People can drive through these areas in their cars or, in many cases, in buses or trains operated by the zoos. The largest of these zoos is the San Diego Wild Animal Park in California, which covers 1,800 acres [728 hectares].

Display and care of animals In the past, zoos crowded animals into small, dark, dirty cages. Shock, disease, and poor treatment killed many of the animals within a few months after their arrival at a zoo. Modern zoos, however, are different. Animals are displayed in settings that often are quite similar to their homes in the wild. Many animals are no longer kept in cages. They live in large areas with trees, plants, pools of water, and, in some cases, waterfalls. These areas are usually surrounded by deep ditches, which keep the animals from leaving their "island." The Bronx Zoo in New York City was the first to enclose many different animals in one area. In its African Plains section, the zoo has birds, reptiles, and mammals that normally live together in Africa. Many other zoos now use this same concept.

Birds are usually displayed in large, enclosed areas called aviaries. Some of these aviaries are enclosed by vertical strands of thin wire which, at a distance, cannot be seen. Animals that would not normally survive the weather and temperature of the zoo are kept in special, climate-controlled buildings that imitate conditions in the wild. Many animals are active at night and sleep during the day (see NOCTURNAL BEHAVIOR). Some zoos have solved this problem by keeping these animals in bright, white light at night and in red light during the day. This makes the animals switch their cycles so that they are active during the day when the zoo has most of its visitors.

Most larger zoos have a full-time veterinary staff that examines and treats the animals (see VETERINARY MEDICINE). Some zoos even have a hospital for sick animals and a nursery for baby animals. All the animals are fed specially designed diets to meet their nutritional needs. Some animals, such as birds, are fed several times a day, while others, such as some reptiles, need to be fed only once or twice a week. All zoos have a trained professional staff that watches over the animals and ensures their safety. Most zoos also have trained guides to lead tours or provide information about the animals to visitors.

History of zoos Since ancient times, people have kept animals for display. The earliest zoo was established in Egypt in about 1500 B.C. Several hundred years later, the Greeks used zoos as places where students could learn about animals and plants. The Romans kept wild animals for use in public fights. Many wealthy Romans even established their own personal zoos. During the Middle Ages in Europe, zoos, like all aspects of science, were generally ignored. As a result, there were very few collections of living wild animals at that time. In 1519, the

ZOO—Shows
Modern zoos often put on shows by dolphins and whales. They help to keep the animals alert and content, as well as provide educational entertainment for visitors.

Spaniards found a large zoo that had been established by the Aztec Indians in Mexico. Although small zoos were started throughout Europe during the next two hundred years, most were unpopular because the animals were treated so badly.

The oldest zoo still in existence is the Schönbrunn Zoo, established in Austria in 1765. The Madrid (Spain) Zoo opened in 1775. The Paris (France) Zoo was established in 1793. The first true zoo, however, was started in 1826 by the Zoological Society of London (England). This zoo was the first to have animals from all parts of the world.

The first zoo in the United States was the Central Park Zoo in New York City. It opened in 1865 and is still in operation. The Philadelphia (Pennsylvania) Zoo opened in 1874. It started the world's first children's zoo in 1938. The only federally funded zoo in the United States was established by Congress in 1889. It is the National Zoological Park in Washington, D.C. The first Canadian zoo opened in Toronto, Ontario, in 1887. By 1900, there were zoos in several major North American cities. Today, there are more than 150 zoos throughout the United States and Canada.
See also ZOOLOGY.

ZOOLOGY (zō ŏl′ə jē) Zoology is the branch of biology that deals with the study of animals. There are at least fourteen well-known areas of specialization within zoology. These include entomology (the study of insects), ornithology (the study of birds), taxonomy (the naming and classifying of animals), anatomy, and morphology (examination of the form and structure of animals), pathology (the study of animal diseases), cytology (the study of cells), histology (the study of tissues), embryology (the study of the development of an animal from a fertilized egg). Genetics, physiology, ecology, psychology, and paleontology are other divisions.
See also BIOLOGY.

ZYGOTE (zī′gōt′) A zygote is a cell produced by the union of two gametes, or sex cells (see GAMETE). It is formed during sexual reproduction and is sometimes thought of as a fertilized egg. A zygote has the full (diploid) number of chromosomes—half from each gamete. A zygote develops into an embryo which, in turn, grows into a fully developed organism.
See also CHROMOSOME; EMBRYO; FERTILIZATION; REPRODUCTION.

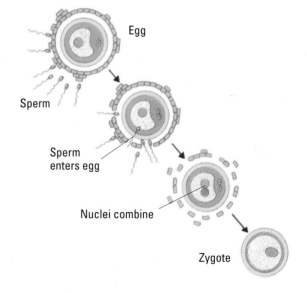

ZYGOTE
A zygote forms after a sperm enters an egg and fertilizes it.